PRETTY WILD

PRETTY WILD

THE MOST HONEST DIARY
ABOUT MEN, WOMEN AND SEX
YOU'LL EVER READ

ANVAR KHAN

BLACK & WHITE PUBLISHING

First published 2004
by Black & White Publishing Ltd
99 Giles Street, Edinburgh EH6 6BZ

ISBN 1 84502 020 0

British Library Cataloguing in Publication Data:
A catalogue record for this book is available
from the British Library.

Cover design: www.henrysteadman.com

Printed and bound by Creative Print & Design

To everyone smart enough to begin this book armed with a glass of wine; a toast please, to Keith, my equal, to Naila, my dear sister, and to my smart, funny, feisty girlfriends. Raise your glass now . . . to health, wealth, happiness, friendship and most importantly, to Love!

To Morven Cameron, my quondam English teacher who sadly died before I could thank her for singling me out at class and berating me quite ruthlessly for slacking; to Tom Shields, who helped me through the cat flap into journalism, a debt to you, sir; and thanks to my agent Annette K Green, my publisher Campbell Brown and my editor at the Scottish News of the World, Bob Bird — brave souls who seem to have much faith in me as a writer.

PRETTY WILD

13 July 2003
7.15am

The man is twitching and snuffling like a bear under a tranquilliser.

I feel pretty sedated too. Well, it's early. I'm not a morning person and I'm definitely not happy with my mussed big hair. And I'm ignoring the mobile, although it's ringing and has been for eight minutes.

Let me introduce myself. My name is Anvar Khan and I'm a professional media whore. TV, radio, columns, I do 'em all, and some would say brazenly. I'm five foot two-and-a-half inches tall. I have black hair, brown eyes, and have a 34F chest. I'm three-quarters breast. In fact, even though I'm single and casually dating, when I look down at my body I realise I've always been part of a couple.

7.17am

I really must change my ring tone. Vivaldi's 'Four Seasons' actually sounds really wanky. I tried Marilyn Manson's 'Mobscene' but that doesn't translate well into polyphonic tone. I'm sure he doesn't compose on a xylophone.

7.19am

Jesus he's snoring now. All right for some. Bloody phone. Who *is* that?

Severe hangover. As always. The dry sweat of dancing and shagging all night, it feels like a film of plastic on my skin. Where's all the light coming from? Shit. The curtains are open, did we do it in front of the neighbours? Lord, I feel cross-eyed with faint. If this relationship goes right, the birds will be singing to me, instead of noising me up with their mating calls.

This bed honks. Men seem to judge the success of a shag by how much sweat they produce. Will have to turn the mattress.

Damn phone, shut up! I'm hungry. I should probably wait until he's woken and I can offer him, er, what can I offer him? I got a free muesli bar with that box of cornflakes, he can have that.

7.20am

Stop ringing! Oh my HEAD!

Perhaps it's not acceptable to give a man a muesli bar for breakfast, maybe he'd prefer something hot. Well, dammit, he had me.

7.21am

Bloody hell, just because he's fucked me doesn't mean he owns the bed. Wherever he lays a woman is obviously his home.

Everyone goes on about the *Kama Sutra* but there should be a handbook for sleeping positions that work for both of you. Fuck! Okay, okay. There's no way I can get up while his heavy leg's lying across my stomach.

7.22am

Bloody mobile. Electronic tagging, that's what it is. Typical. I hope it's not Jeremy Vine. The show, not the man. Right, I'm answering. Hold on. Where is it? Shit, it's still in my bag in the living room. Move your limb baby. Don't then. Ow, didn't notice that wall before. OW! Stubbed my toe. Bummer! Arse!

There's seems to be some architectural conspiracy stopping

me getting to the front room.

'Anvar, it's me, Anna.'

'Hi babe. I love you, but it's bloody early, what is it? You alright? Is there an emergency?' My eyes are still closed.

'Did you sleep with him?'

'Who?'

'Mikey.'

'Of course I fucking slept with him. Oh, don't worry. I mean I did the right thing, we waited. You know, so he doesn't think I'm easy. I mean, rules of engagement and all that. You have to seem to be a bit of a . . . [yawn] . . . sorry . . . challenge. Why?'

'Oh no, Anvar.' Anna is sighing. 'I heard last night. One of the girls in the loo, you know, when we were reapplying our body glitter.'

'Huh?'

'The Benefit powder puff . . . the one that makes your skin sparkle . . .'

'Yes, yes . . . oh right, yeah. What?'

'Anvar, I'm so sorry, I couldn't get you on your own. I didn't think you'd . . .'

'Anna, my head is really sore . . . I'm still drunk, I . . .'

'Babe,' Anna is almost crying. 'Babe, he's married.'

7.45am

Funny how your life changes in an instant. I'll take my head off the fridge door in a minute. Can't stand here all day. It's kind of cooling though. Better put the moby off too. Can't think. Can't deal with anything. He's married? Mike has a wife? MIKEY has a wife!

Teabags, teabags, milk. Why can't I remember where I put things? I mean, he's actually married?

I must do a washing. Really, must do a washing. Need something to wear tonight, for the party. Need things to wear, daily.

That's it! It's too damn bright. I'm putting on my sunglasses. Where are they? I CAN'T FIND ANYTHING! There. The Ferragamo ones, green hardened plastic with blue tinted lenses, they're a bit Jarvis Cocker but they're okay for the house.

He's lying through there in my bed, I mean, IT is deep in slumber, I mean, he wouldn't be able to sleep so soundly if he had a guilty conscience, right, would he?

I mustn't smoke. Went through 60 last night.

I mean Mike can be annoying. He's not perfect. I don't like his teeth, he wears crap shoes, and I don't like the way he always presumes he knows more than the maître d'. Mike makes a point of telling everyone that Burgundy is actually a white wine and you shouldn't drink the Chateaubriand.

MARRIED? No way. I would have spotted something. I mean, I'm a woman of the world. Mmm . . . tea. I think I've got a pube in the back of my throat. Why is morning telly so bad? Relationship advice coming up? Yeah, I'll phone in. I need a fag, one of my gay male mates who can tell me all about men and why they lie.

No, I couldn't be duped like this.

Fuck it. I'm smoking. Bugger it. Stress an' all. Great, lighter's out of fuel.

7.46am
I'm just sitting here.

7.47am
Must move. Kettle's boiled. Need a lighter.

7.48am
Just can't move at all.

7.50am
I don't feel right about going through someone's pockets. God

I feel dizzy. This standing up stuff is overrated. I must sit down again. No I can't. Too disorientated. I'm pacing. Shit, he has a lot of pockets, this Mr Seven-Piece Suit.

Damn my moby! It's off again. I really, really need a lighter. Who is it now? Everyone knows lunchtime is my breakfast. Fuck, I've got a text. I think I can focus. It's from Sam. Yes, I'll be there. We have to celebrate after all. Tonight seems so far away. Noon seems like a death knell.

7.53am

Anna wouldn't lie to me. She's my friend. She sounds really upset. Who was she talking to in the loo anyhow? CID woman? It'd be a first for women to get that far without conking out on that cracked glass ceiling.

God this is tedious. Nice suit lining. I'm not getting anywhere here. Realise I have my eyes shut behind my sunglasses. Very plush Mikey. Very impressive. Oh, Savile Row.

What's this? Mike's mobile? No, that's not what I want . . . lighter . . . hmmm? Anyone? Nope. Feels like a . . . a ring? A ring . . . strange . . . could be one of those napkin rings . . . he must have been at a dinner or something and mistakenly slipped it into his pocket . . . would be a ring to fit a giant if it was . . . it really feels like a finger ring, well, why wouldn't you be wearing it . . . why . . . I mean . . . erm . . . I don't think I want this in my hands . . . can't be . . . I'm taking my sunglasses off . . . but I don't want to see it . . . it is . . . it's a gold band. What? I can't believe it.

No way. Not me, not me, not again.

The toilet bowl is strangely reassuring. I haven't had my head down it for a long time.

Ugh.

Thoughts piling up like a motorway crash. Spewing out of me like this thin, yellowy vomit. What a detox. Feel like I'm regurgitating my past. It was only last month. The same thing happened. Me left on my own, again. Fucked and fucked over. The scene is living in my head like a bewildered rat, banging off the corners of my cranium.

Here it is, coming at me, as my gut heaves. There we were, only six weeks ago, Seamus and me, sitting together, drinking, laughing, scared to talk of love.

Rewind a few weeks to 4 June

7pm

'You sure you're doing the right thing?' I'm asking, with an authoritative air that belies years of personally arsing up and in a spectacularly Hollywood way.

'The time is right, Anvar, I want to settle down. Me and Sarah, we have our ups and downs, I have my doubts but I think it'll be okay.'

'But you know, Seamus, we can still be friends when you're married, can't we?'

Why is he looking so sad? Can he see his tax bill in that pint of lager?

'No Anvar, not as close as we have been.'

I didn't hear that. I did not hear that rejection of me. Know he's the only man I've ever really liked.

'Seamus you can't dump your mates because you are going to have a wife! I really didn't think that of you, you know? Hen-pecked. I mean, really!'

Typical. A woman gets her claws into a guy and he's suddenly forbidden from having platonic female relationships.

But still, I feel like I'm falling down a bottomless pit, and the panic won't go away until I'm too dead to feel it.

10.30pm

And . . . Seamus and I, well, we're trashed.

'Maybe things would have been different between us, if we had met under different circumstances,' I'm saying, politely, like a Victorian.

'You mean, Anvar, if I had met you before I met my fiancé, you mean if you weren't going out with David, my best mate?'

I know why they are called circumstances; because an invisible rope entwines you slowly until you are restrained and imprisoned.

7

And now the table's covered in beer. And yes, Seamus nearly smashed his glass. Everybody's looking.

'Why are you slamming your tumbler?' I'm hissing. He's angry; it's the first sign I've ever seen of a passion for me.

'Anvar, I'm going to be married. What's done is done. I can't see you when I'm married because, it's not appropriate.'

I'm a spitfire.

'What exactly, to use your carefully chosen word, is inappropriate about our friendship?'

I'm begging him here to spell it out, to explain to me, to tell me why during years of friendship, his arms have always lingered around me.

This man. I can see him. As a man. Not as a pal. I want to stroke the greying hair on his temples. I want to know what it would feel like to kiss him, the only man I've ever truly adored as a person. The guy I've always sparked off.

This is our last chance. I know it, he knows it.

'Need a slash.' I run off to the loo.

No toilet roll. Arse. Oh well. Staggering a bit as I'm balancing on stilettos and pulling up tight jeans. Fall out of cubicle. Stare at self in mirror. Look at myself in the eye. If we do this, then it's meant to be, if it doesn't happen, then it's not. Huh, the reasoning of the coward at heart.

Back to table. Seamus looks tense and upset.

'Anvar, it's not that I'm leaving you, it's just that I can't handle . . . I need to concentrate on my marriage and . . . I can't let anyone down . . .'

We are fucked. I'm still with his best friend. The invitations have been sent out. It's all too complicated.

'Sleep with me Seamus.'

5 June
9.30am

Arms around me, one hand holding mine. Been awake for ages. A clear day. Beautiful. I am content. Nuzzling his temples, kissing his glorious head. I turn over. He groans sleepily. Smiles. Such a fierce face. A face I admit, I saw a million times in my mind, before I saw him for real, in a moment you are only ever granted once in a lifetime if you are lucky.

My gorgeous man. My love. My equal. The passion I have always craved. My spiritual fucking home.

If You're Going To Shag The Groom, Don't Go To The Wedding

7 June
4.30pm

In a big hat. Well, it's an important do, isn't it? It's black. I'm wearing black. Might as well be in a coffin. That is how I feel.

And everyone thinks my funeral gear is merely a fucking style statement. I mean, am I that superficial?

David keeps flashing me filthies. Perhaps this morning wasn't the best time to tell him he's chucked. Him being the best man and all that.

Church looks nice tho'. The birds are singing outside, the flowers are nodding happily at the couple at the altar, I can see the flowers being blown on by the breeze, outside. Outside. Where I should be. I am the outsider. I am Camilla fucking Parker Bowles. I have lost him. I have lost more now than what I was scared of. Kinda symbolic that he's standing with his back to me, I'm shut out. Forever.

And now it's over, words of commitment have been spoken, and he is walking back up the aisle, and she is on his arm, in a blancmange number, drinking up all those sentimental familial tears, dressed up like Tinkerbell, and I feel hateful. I feel robbed. I wish her all the misery any human being isn't ever entitled to.

I hope her hands bleed when she does the dishes, I hope her fragrant vanilla scent turns to the smell of ash, I hope she develops sudden and unexpected hair and weight gain and turns into Chewbacca, I hope her smug, satisfied smiles become a bitter grimace, I hope her nudity eventually disgusts him, I hope she bores him because she always wants the lights off during sex, I hope her joyful, happy heart that gloats and parades before me is wizened and blackened by waning love, as mine has been.

And parents are crying and clasping their hands together, beaming with pride, sending another two people on their way to wedded bliss, and this is my paradise lost.

I will not meet his eye. I will not look at him again. I will forget him.

7pm

Oh God. Wedding speeches about stars and rainbows and eternal love and clouds and angels singing. Get me outta here.

I am an evil spell.

'Hi, I'm Mikey. Fancy another glass of champagne?' Don't mind if I do.

13 July
7.57am

And now me, myself and I, and a guy called Mikey, well, we're here again.

Spittle on the pan. Am retching and there's nothing left to bring up. How the hell did I get here? This just isn't dignified. I have a life, a career, friends, I'm chubby but I'm not that fat, and I keep waking up with Mr Wrong, like I deserve it.

It's all pure dramarama.

I just want a normal life. I must get my act together, I must go out, and meet new people, new men, instead of dreaming of a Mr Right, whoever he is, but who hopefully owns a big mansion and a garden where I can have big house parties.

7.58am

I have such bad karma. I must have done something in a past life, the problem with that being there's bugger all I can do about it now.

What was I? A killer of married men? Now they keep turning up in my bed, every time it's like waking up beside a horse's head. Instant guilt. Just add Anvar, and mix.

In my defence, Sir, Lord, Your Honour, the Great Almighty, Buddha, Mohammed etc. . . . if I have slept with a married man before, I didn't know about it. I was seduced in ignorance of what was the truth. Those trips to Ikea and runs to the beach, the sort of stuff families do, I had no idea that was going on behind my back.

The criminal intent was theirs, m'lord.

Marriage. Men who are about to be married and men who are married. They just love me. Not.

What did I do when I realised they were, er, taken? M'lord? Ummm, I, er, I, er, well, I had a think about it and I, well, I decided it was their problem not mine. I mean, I didn't take any vows did I? Was I the one who stood in church in front of God, er, You, in fact, and a battalion of parents and promised to be faithful?

I'm the innocent party mate, it's not my fault a man can't resist a short skirt. I mean, regular pussy or a bit of strange? Who's your daddy?

7.59am

Fuck, I mean, people say a woman can attract the wrong men. How exactly can she do this? It seems to be a very under-rated female skill, this ability to choose men who are bad for us.

Why does Mr Wrong have such a magnetic pull? So many Mr Wrongs do not a Mr Right make.

7.59 and a half am

Actually, even for a man I thought was right for me, I was the wrong woman at the wrong time. Wasn't I, Seamus?

There is no moral ground.

The whole episode is insulting. I have no control over who

falls into my bed and fucks with my head.

I've knocked back so many married men, and have been decent enough to do so, only to find I've inadvertently slept with some more!

Fidelity must be going out of fashion. First time I've been SO not with the latest trend.

8am

Not like I'm asking to be treated badly.

8.01am

It's me. Definitely moi. Maybe guys really want more of a doormat and the challenge is fucking over a woman like me, twisting me into something broken.

There's no way shagging me when you have a wife isn't a genius means of humiliating me. And then there's having sex when you are about to be married. Yes. I must fill their boots as well as I wear Manolo.

I don't know what to think. All I know is that married men think I'm an ideal bit on the side. Why is this the case? Why do they think I'm a pushover? You could get really paranoid about this kinda thing.

Is it my nose? Is it my hair? Am I a flashback to a tortured youth?

I just sense I must be a trigger; they see me and are set off on a subconscious journey and they will swear to their wives they were swept along on and that ultimately they weren't responsible for their actions. I must really fuck with some heavy childhood issues.

8.02am

I felt like Mikey's wife going through his pockets there. If I wanted to feel like a suspicious housewife I'd be one.

Poor bitch. Come to think of it, maybe she knows he's a slut and she doesn't have enough money to leave. Oh no! She's a woman in crisis. Vulnerable. And me a feminist too. I will be damned. Put in stocks. I should be doing some kind of charity work for her kind, some spare hours spent on voluntary support for women whose trust is abused by men. You know, just to put something back in their lives, and not just return their husbands.

Maybe she gave up her life and job to be with him. Oh no! That's horrendous! She could even be disabled, or mentally ill, or kept in a basement in the dark and fed gruel. Maybe she has money, is a millionairess, and he lives off her, beats her at night, steals from her bank account in the morning.

Or . . .

Perhaps she's one of those women who get married in love and trust and give up their jobs and therefore their incomes. She hates him now but can't leave. She knows he's a scumbag but she still loves him. Oh God, kids!!! Mikey might have a baby. He might have several. He may even have babies with other women who don't know he has a wife! It gets worse and worse.

8.03am
This is really bad form.

8.04am
By the way, it's my birthday today. I'm 36. Tonight it's my party and I will fuck everyone if I want to. Maybe I'll take Sam up on his offer. I have other options. Don't need that bollocking two-bit piece of fake lying next door.

Although . . .

It's probably not a good idea shagging another man, having sex with men is what got me into this situation in the first place. I could go at it again but I'd be a lemming.

PRETTY WILD

8.05am

Euch . . . oh here he comes, in my dressing gown, lord of the manor, and looking very rough I would say. Morning dearest darling sweetness *Asshole! Arse! Cunt!*, no, I didn't hear you get up. Sure you can have a shower. Nope, I'm okay. No, I'm just hungover. You know I don't like the smell of vodka on my breath in the morning, makes me queasy. Makes me sick. No, no, no, no, no, there's nothing wrong. Thanks for asking. Of course I would tell you if there was. I mean, we have no secrets do we, honey bunny?

Loser.

Yes, of course the sex was great. In fact it really was bloody, bloody awesome. And don't you just love the smell of come in the morning? Yeah, I'm glad we waited too. One shouldn't rush into these things, should one? You gotta know who you are dealing with, and backing off, well, it's respectful, isn't it? I mean there are crazies out there.

And you're one of them. Prick.

What? You'll call me? When you get into work? Oh that's so sweet, angel. Yep Friday's good for me too.

Play him along, string him along, need time here, to think, I mean shredding his trousers or even cutting off Mr Choo Choo is a bit cliché. Need a more original revenge strategy than doing a Bobbit on his little hobbit.

Sure Mike. Bye. No, I'm not turning away from you. No, don't be daft. I'm fine. A-b-s-o-l-u-t-e-l-y fine.

Pranny! The man is a serious prat and an exceptional fucking fanny!

I have morning breath, you know, that's right, I am stinking, all dog breath and poo poo, yes, my mouth tastes like I've eaten shite, really does, last thing you'd want to do is stick your tongue in there oh no. It'd be like licking out a doberman's arsehole. Really would. No I'm not being crude. No I am not joking.

15

GET OFF ME!

You really don't want to snog me.

No, get off me Mike, I'm serious. Look how serious I am, I'm so serious I could be a terrorist threat.

Look, if you must know, that's it, you asked for it, the truth? Okay. I've just puked. I've BOAKED! Ha! Ha? Get me now? Wanna taste it? No, didn't think you would. No, don't wanna kiss me now do ya? No, I've got mints, thanks, fine. No, I've got plenty. I can go buy some more later. Extra strong mints, yes, you are right, they'll do the trick. No, really, don't worry, think there's Tic Tacs somewhere.

See you then.

Call me.

8.06am

Think my stomach is going to fly out my mouth.

8.07am

Not feeling so good. I'm putting the damn moby off. I fear I may stay in bed all day.

2pm

Still in bed.

Sighing.

I am a rational person. I am a reasonable person. I prefer logic to emotion, I am Spock.

What I'm proposing is this. I need to know the full extent of how much Mikey is married. For factual reasons. Okay, okay, I need any excuse not to feel this paranoid. If he's not married then what happened with Seamus is a blip. A mere dip of bad luck, and I can stop feeling persecuted by unfaithful guys.

I need to be professional about this. I need clear information. I'm a journalist. I am a news gatherer. I am a hunter. I can nose around.

14 July
12 noon

They should invent a shampoo for after sex, a sort of post-coital all-in-one.

Hey, do you have problems with tangled and matty hair, after a man has pulled you about a bed all night?

Try Fuck and Go.

Hey, I'm Anvar and I don't have to worry about tugs and wearing an unexpected bird's nest. This amazing product means I can just get up in the morning and go straight to work without looking as if I've been well and truly shagged.

I use Fuck and Go! I just Fuck! And then I Go!

The ideal hair restorative protein all-in-one conditioner complete with anti-frizz serum. Fuck and Go. For today's modern woman.

Shit, some women stare at the ceiling, make shopping lists, I make up fucking adverts.

Ahhh, aahhhhhh, aaahhhhhh . . . nope.

Wish Sam would stop peeking up at me. I'm shaking my head to tell him it hasn't worked yet, and to keep going.

I don't think he's got an erection anymore.

I'm going to have to do that Donatella Versace thing. She uses olive oil for everything; it moisturises, it's a cleanser. I'll put that on my hair. Wrap a hot towel around it.

AAAAhhhhhhh . . . uh . . . uh . . . nope.

Sam's very sweet. He's been going down on me now for nearly . . . what's the time? Is THAT the time! Fuck! He's been lapping away at me for three hours.

I remember him saying he cared deeply about the female orgasm.

Oh fuck.

Uh . . . uhuh . . . huh . . . oh . . . oh . . . uh-huh . . . yes . . . mmmm . . . oh . . . yes . . . yes . . . yesyesyesyesyesyesyesyes . . . YES! God. YES! YES! JESUS!!!!

I'm faking it. I'm actually faking it. Not because he's crap in bed, but because I think I'm taking advantage of his good nature.

He's a lovely man. And God he's been doing his best. Think it's polite to make him happy.

He looks really pleased.

12.25pm

The guy's turned me into a fucking virgin. This is a first for me. I've faked it on a one-night stand. Ridiculous. I usually only fake fur, and even then I prefer the real thing.

I know the score. I know what to do. The men you use for casual sex are the men you get to make you come all the time, because you don't care how they perceive you. You use them like sex slaves. I know, I know. Women are fucked up. It's an irony that we save our lies about coming for the one we love.

'Twas a great birthday party, mind you.

1.32pm

Thinking about Mikey. Can't let it go. That's it! Enough fretting, enough supposing, enough of all this dreary sulky shit. What am I, a victim? Decide to make an investigative report into Mikey's life.

24 July
5.30pm

It's taken me all day to organise a car. Couldn't find my driving license. Not a great passport photo, I have to say. Why is there always only ever a booth in Woolworths? Do they have the franchise on anyone who needs ID? Nearly a fiver for four mini-me's. A rip-off. I tried a different pose for each one. I mean I'm a professional. I've done publicity shots before.

5.45pm

I'm really worried about these photos. The lighting's really bad, as if I've been snapped in a storm. I look really sinister, like when I wear pink, y'know, same thing. You just know something's not right, it's like I've been dressed by someone else and handed a day release pass.

Yep, I look Eastern, but kinda sociopathic-looking, as if I have a secret hatred of the world. If I go to Hollywood with this as a passport shot, they'll direct me straight to Guantanamo Bay. Greta Garbo always told her lighting designers she needed to feel the heat on her face. You just can't get the service you need nowadays.

6.20pm

Okay, seeing as it's illegal to drive and phone at the same time, I guess it's probably out of order to read a map too. I'll stop here. Oh there's a pattiserie. Kinda peckish.

It's called Apostrophe? And it's a café too! Fuck, imagine having a hot date and saying yeah, I'll meet you in Apostrophe! And what happens when they own a few of them, where do they put the apostrophe then?

6.21pm

Maybe I should stock up, it's going to be a long night. All those cops on the TV, Americans in their cars, scoffing hot dogs and supersize coffee and doughnuts. I don't think I can get that much into character. I think I'll get some couscous and a little spring water.

Right, I'm where? Jolly good. No, it's not. I'm looking to go north. Jesus, forgot to indicate. I don't drive, I aim.

6.32pm

It was really nice of that woman at the library to help me look up the voters' register, and the internet people finder is such a help. I'm really glad she saw me on *Richard and Judy*. She's a woman's woman. I know this because she kept talking about *The Judy and Richard Show*.

Celebrity always makes such a good impression.

What time is it? Seven minutes past six. So he leaves work around quarter to, and I don't think this is his gym night.

7.30pm

God, this is dull. My arse hurts. Been sitting far too long. Just feels like it's swollen like a baboon. I can't get out and walk around, someone will see me. I'm sure that's his flat.

No one tells you stakeouts are so boring. Although I think Cagney and Lacey mentioned it. Did their nails. Jesus, plonked here, I'm even boring myself.

7.32pm

Oh, moby's off! Arse! Twenty-five big arses! Twenty-six including my own. Why are you ducking down onto the passenger seat?! You twat, woman! It's a phone Anvar, a phone, not a person. Oh no! Private call. Oh, God, what if it's him? What will I say, that I'm parked outside his home, like a detective?

'Hi Babe.'

Phew, it's Anna calling from the BBC.

'Anvar, you okay?' Anna is sounding worried.

'Of course I am, why wouldn't I be?'

It is occurring to me that what I'm doing can't possibly be classed as normal behaviour, which means, in actual fact, that I am really upset.

'Are you sure you're okay?' Anna, the disbeliever.

'Yes, I'm fine, absolutely fine, I'm good, really, really good. I've got my health, my friends, my career, I mean what more do you need?'

Anna's silences are really quite deep.

'But enough about me, what about you?' My tone sounds

light, airy, even, in fact, I would say, cheery.

Anna's been cut off. No, moby says the call's connected. I'm not giving in to the silence. I've said my bit, I've been convincing, it's her problem if she doesn't believe me.

'Anvar, what are you doing?'

'What? At this moment, you mean?'

'Yes.' Dunno why she's going all assertive on me. I'm not doing anything wrong. It's a free country. People can stalk other people if they want to.

'Right at this moment?' I'm sounding nervous, must stop that.

'Yes, Anvar, right now.'

'Oh, you know, sitting. I'm sitting. I have sitting-bottom syndrome, and all that. It hurts.'

'What?'

'My arse is sore.'

'Anvar, are you trying to tell me something? That you've done and swore you'd never do. Have you taken it up the arse?'

'Certainly not.'

'Are you on drugs?'

I've got to come clean. I'm sounding weirder than what I'm actually doing.

I'll keep it basic.

'Look Anna.'

I'll keep it simple.

'When a guy comes your way you know little about him. Agreed?'

'Well, yeah.'

She'll understand.

'And it takes years to know a person. And all the time you're with him, you learn about him, and everything he says you have to take at face value. Right?'

'Sure.' Anna's concentrating very, very hard, I can tell. See, she gets it!

'Well, there's a short cut you know, that you can take, so you know who you're dealing with. I'm not being paranoid, no, it's just that there might be another reason why there was a wedding ring in Mike's pocket . . .'

'Anvar . . .'

'And if there is I have to know. I have to know so I can work out what I'm going to do. Look, I'm just doing what any reporter does, it's just, I suppose, that most journalists aren't this close to their subject.'

'Anvar where are you?'

'I'm outside Mike's flat. In a car. Rented. It's a Sierra.'

'Anvar, get out of there!'

'Why? Look I need to know if he's married. I need to know this! What else can I do?'

'Anvar this is really bad.'

'No! It's not! It's cheaper than a private dick. Knowledge is power, we know that. I need to know if he's done this to me. Anna, I need to know. For real.'

I'm a mess. I know I'm a mess. Jeez, if I could only grab a little of myself back. If only it hadn't been my birthday when I found out. If only he wasn't fucking with my head.

'Anvar.' Anna is being gentle. 'Anvar, don't do this to yourself babe. I understand what you're doing and why you're doing it, but Mike's married. You have to accept that. This . . . what you're doing . . . you have to let go. Anvar, this kind of obsession, it will destroy you. Okay he's hurt you. You have to move on. Anvar, start up the engine, get out of there, before he sees you. Or his wife does.'

That's the thing about men, when they lie to you, they can turn you into a psycho.

4 August
8am

Boiling an egg. Three minutes, no problem. Oh God, no second hand on my watch? Does anyone actually own an egg-timer? Or did they go out with the fondue sets?

Leaning my forehead on the fridge door. Keep finding myself doing this, 'tis very cooling.

I wonder if I should leave Glasgow? Just leave. Go. A big fuck-off bye bye. Have an adventure. See some sights.

Always meant to move at some point. Now's probably the time, yet it's like running away, tho'. Aw c'mon Khan.

No one will know that. I mean, we all know that if you take your career at all seriously, you have to 'do' London. Huh! London sounds like the office slut.

It might make a bigger media tart of me. Mind you, that's okay. Never had any credibility to lose.

Yes, the bright lights of the metropolis are so dazzling, the future they offer looks very bright.

Okay, okay, Anvar, admit it. You're on a mission. You want your equal. A lover. Another chance. You want to start again.

Feel I'm wiser now. Fitter in the heart. I can do this. I can move away from here.

Can see him now, Mikey, crying, waving a white hanky, snuffling. Remembering what a gal I was and how much he misses me. But no. I will go.

Men are a distraction, and some men are even a distraction from other men. Plenty more fish in the sea. I know, because I've caught quite a few and have thrown them back.

Damn. Burnt the egg. It's black and cracking, pieces spurting and farting off like shrapnel. Sorry hen, you wasted your time laying that one. Often feel the same myself.

8.34am

Off downstairs to get the post. Oh no, bills, bills, bills and ugh, credit card statements. Well, a woman can't live on sex toys alone.

Oooh, a package.

8.36am

Wow, och the sweetie.

Anna's such a love. Sent me over an emergency package; essentials oils, bubble bath, nail polish and a book called *Women Who Love Too Much*.

8.37am

I'm a girl! It's official. Nothing like the zen pleasure of taking time out not to care anymore and just busying yourself with orange sticks and face packs. My self-esteem needs a little pampering.

8.38am

I think your self-esteem is all you have. Stops you taking crap, helps you walk away. Funny how when a woman feels low some guy always gets a bargain.

1pm

Feel depressed again. That means I'll be cheap tonight.

3.30pm

Anyway, there'll be loads more shags down there in London. Might even find the man of my dreams.

I mean it's a numbers game, innit? The more men you go through, the more chance you have of finding love.

Yes, my future awaits me.

Dunno why I've just taken to lying under my quilt.

4pm

Might get up.

Can't be arsed. Still in bed. Where's my stuff? Yes. Good. I have 40 Marlboro Lights, two bottles of cava and Mary J Blige's 'No More Pain' on CD replay. Shit. It's only 4.48pm. Cosy here tho'. Think I'll cry a little.

7 August
6pm
Sam's calling.

'Hi Anvar, how are you?'

Why does everyone sound as if they're asking after Anvar post-rehab?

'Fine.'

'Look, about the sex . . . I didn't want to call before but I didn't know what to do . . .'

'Sam it was fine . . . no . . . it was wonderful, really good. One of the best one-night stands I've ever had.'

'I see. That's all I wanted to know Anvar.' Click. Burr.

He's hung up. He's actually hung up on me.

10 August
9pm
Miss Seamus. Feel guilty about Sam. Feel bruised post-Mike. Too many emotions are fighting for attention. Never shag a man who's your friend and who also happens to love you. Never sleep with a man you love when he's about to be married. And never shag a married man who you happen to be in lust with. See? I'm always learning. Life isn't complicated at all. It's just fabulous to be a 21st-century girl.

12 August

1pm

Bloody moby. Private call. No trace. Shit. Here goes.

'Anvar.'

'Ermmmm . . . ermmmm . . .'

It's Mikey.

'You've not been taking my calls. I've left numerous voicemails. Where are you?'

Having a champagne lunch with Johnny Depp. Basking in the glow of a successful movie script and the LA sun.

'In Glasgow.'

'What you doing?'

Nosey twat.

I'm manacled to the bed. Having my toenails painted by a naked Willem Dafoe.

'Watering my plants.'

Silence. Why does everyone keep going quiet on me?

'Anvar.' Mikey sounds scared. 'You don't have any plants. They died, remember?'

Jesus, the bloody nerve.

'Don't tell me I don't have plants. I have lots of plants, ferns and begonias, and that Japanese thing, Bonsai ones. I bought them. By myself. All by myself, with my own money in my own time.'

How dare he pick me up on anything? How can he question me about anything, and in my own home?

'Call you later.'

Help.

11.04pm

I've got money. I'm successfully single. I have nice things. Not like I'm a failure or anything is it?

Hmmm . . .

Have invented a slogan to describe my life. Will get it engraved on a magnet and stick it on the fridge and look at it in those personal and philosophical moments. It goes:

My life is empty but my wardrobe is full.

12 midnight
I think I'm becoming a freak but I think and I hope and I pray that at least I make it work for me.

27 August
2pm
Oh here he is, shining with pride, clutching the champagne list.

'Lovely, thanks.'

Kelvin's not bad I suppose. He's dapper enough. Newspaper editors usually are.

Have a list of features I can write for him. Need extra cash. For the get-to-London fund. Yep, I'm going. Done everything and everyone here.

Kelvin's a bit keen. Have the impression he's trying to impress me as a man, rather than as a boss. Still, I was never one of those women who think that because a man wants to sleep with you, that's some kind of compliment. I mean, they'll shag anything. Lord, I'm a train wreck.

'The bubbles list is very reasonable. Have a look while I go to the little boys' room.'

Nae problem.

'It's just that I have to go wee.'

'Uh-huh.'

Can't help noticing that Kelvin's mouthing words like a woman talking about having problems 'downstairs' in the hysterectomy department.

'Will you be okay when I'm gone?'

He seems very concerned. What does he think is going to happen to me?

'Yes.'

'It's just that I must go, you know.'

God, he's winking at his pelvis.

'You must order bubbles when I've gone.'

'Ermm . . . yeah, I can do that.'

'Is it really all right if I go?'

'Yes Kelvin. No really. On you go. Kelvin, I mean we all have to go sometime.'

He's smiling like I've granted him his greatest wish.

'Okay.'

The little boys' room? Am I his mommy?

4.45pm

Kelvin's looking quite attractive, actually. Hic.

5pm

Another bottle of Bolly? Why, sure, Kelvin, I would like that very much. Oh, I can write later. Let's live for the moment. Because, I mean, tomorrow is another day. Christ, I sound like Scarlett O'fucking Hara.

6.45pm

'Bubbles?' If I could slap my hand for reaching out to accept more drink I would. I really, really, really, really would.

Jesus, in another bar, round the Italian Centre I think. I don't remember walking round. I've never been here before. How am I going to find the toilet?

7.10ish pm

'I am absolutely fine with women wearing sexy underwear. I find it very attractive,' Kelvin's saying.

Huh? How did we get to talk about underwear? What's Kelvin on about?

'For instance, I love the way your red bra is just peeking over your black suit jacket in a very subtle yet peek-a-boo way. It's very classy.'

'Oh, is it showing?'

I really don't like this direction. He was so shy earlier. It's like being signed up for a war you don't agree with; I'm an unconscious objector, much too pissed to refuse to go along with what's happening.

'Yes, I like to wear it myself. As you can see. Hic. All women want to feel sexy, and, you know, I'm being really, really, really, REALLY feminist about that . . . this . . . because . . . you know. We are sexy. Women ARE sexy, all the time. I know this . . . that . . . because I am one.'

What to do? He's running away too much here, dirty boy. God, I'm so drunk.

Got to centre, take the power back.

Shit! We're in the Rogano! I recognise it now. All these couples mooching about. It's like being single and holidaying in a honeymoon resort by mistake. Motherfuckers.

'It's very sophisticated.'

'Yes, my point EXACTLY. Well done Kelvin. You're right, absolutely right.'

Mental note: What's sophisticated, again?

'I know a little place not far from here, which specialises in very classy lingerie. I think they have thongs from Paris,' he's saying.

'Oooh . . . Paris. Hic.'

'BA do very reasonable return deals, under £300 including B&B.'

'Kelvin, I know this sounds strange and just not very cosmopolitan . . . but . . . and I know journalists should be able to bugger off at any point and do a story . . . mean, our editors, my editor, because you ARE an editor, well, we could just . . . have to go, really, really, when we're asked . . . just go . . . hic. I don't have my passport with me.'

Mental note: £300 equals ten bottles of champagne.

8pm

'Just away to the . . .' he's mouthing the words and I'm mouthing them along with him, 'little boys' room'.

Can't focus on all the guys leaving the loo, who zip themselves up as an afterthought. Why do men do that? They just want to get 'it' out, their little soldier, their sword, their wee Alexander, all the time, don't they?

Oh, here he is. Kelvin's flushed with booze. All pink, like a boiled spot. Nope. I'm not even going to check for a pee stain. I mean he's bought me bubbles all night, wouldn't be fair to check.

He's old, bloody old, probably can't help going all the time. Not so much fighting forty as fending off sixty.

'But Anvar, you didn't answer my question.'

'Huh? Hic.' No, don't think he's dribbled.

'Do you wear thongs?'

'Why, yes, I do.' Scarlett O'Hara again. Rhett was a mature man, wasn't he?

'Let's go, Anvar.'

28 August
12 noon

No, no, no, no, no, this is not the way it's supposed to be. No! There have to be decent men in the world. There have to be. If not, it means that every woman in love is a liar. Which could be true because we can lie very well. I'm still in bed. My calves ache from wearing heels all night.

12.05pm

Mikey lied to me. Maybe we're all lying, and for what? A little marital security, the experience of being a mother or a father, some extra-curricular sex on tap? It's a scary thought that romantic love could be based on mutual bullshit.

12.06pm
Worried about my lifestyle. Too much alcohol, too many men.

Us single thirtysomething women, with our no-strings-attached sex life, we're penis fodder.

12.07pm
Men and women are not supposed to be together. We're too different. At least gay folk know that and have the sense to sleep with each other.

This much is clear. From what I see of men, I don't want one of my own.

You know, I think I'm being forced to make a choice here; go my own way, a kinda slut-lite, or hang about waiting for one of them to prove to me they are worthy investing in.

Nah! No man is worth being hurt for.

I've thought of a new fridge magnet philosophy to stick on my freezer, they're little sayings I make up now and again.

Every time my heart was broke, by someone else,
it was all because I was waiting for you, to come along,
and do it again.

12.08pm
Must get up.

I don't know whether I'm still drunk or if my mania is my natural state of grace.

I want the real deal, if I ever fall for a man, I want to feel love. I don't want to be given it, accept it, respect it or even like it. I want to feel what it feels like to love a man. So much you'd take a bullet for him.

12.10pm

Oh, but look at the pretty things.

I love the tissue wrap you get in boxes of lingerie. Wow. Purple silk thong from Aubade with lace and a bow detail, a Rigby and Peller bra and panties set. Sheer Kenzo knickers in cream with turquoise embroidery.

Kelvin's flesh is weak but his wallet is willing. His plastic is probably the hardest thing about him.

4pm

I'm up and at it. This week's *News of the World* column: Why Modern Girls Should Never Say 'I'll Pay'.

I've got a bloody nerve.

From Why Women Are Always Right to How To Get Over An Ex, my work reads like the fucking Waltons compared to my real day-to-night shenanigans.

I mean, you can say you shagged a guy when you were somewhat inebriated and acceptably put it down to a drunken mistake, but how many of us can say when we were legless we made a guy we hardly know buy us expensive lingerie? I tell you, the gifts make you feel dirtier than a quick dumb fuck ever has.

Dunno what the score is with Kelvin.

My head's sore. I've been in training for years but I still get a nightmare hangover.

6pm

I feel like shit, I really do. What am I doing letting a guy buy me underwear? I mean he was nice about it, didn't even try to get into the changing room with me.

7.30pm

I mean, it was nice of him to put me in a taxi too.

7.32pm

That's it, the only reason I don't feel like a prostitute is because I didn't sleep with him.

7.35pm

Going to bed. Never talking to men again. It's all too difficult. It's all too much. I mean, I just want to get on with my work.

8pm

I can be mercenary. In fact, I think I should cultivate a little of it. I mean, I never, ever thought I could be bought, and looking at my new and interesting and exotic new purchases, er gifts, I think I just have been.

3 September

11.30pm

Haven't seen Heidi for months.

'I mean, he fancies my best friend. He comes all the way over from America, and ends up asking her out.'

Heidi's as happy and as personally fulfilled as I am. The feminists sold us a dud.

'I mean I love the American accent . . . that's what attracted me. I just love it.'

'Thought you said you met him online?' I query.

'Yes, but he's American! And he's a bastard! It's too much to take. A double whammy!'

'What?'

We're dancing to 'Gimme! Gimme! Gimme! (A Man After Midnight)', like two aunties at a wedding.

'A fucking double whammy!'

'Don't think they serve that at the bar, Heidi . . .'

'I mean, what do you do if you like a guy? Lock him up? Refuse to let him see your best mates in case he doesn't like you anymore?'

The only other song we are going to get up for is 'I Will Survive'. I know it. I can feel it.

You see, we're standing out like spinsters, fully paid-up members of the club of perpetual disappointment. We're Miss Havisham's children, for God's sake. Or should that be Ms?

4 September
3am

Not that arseholed for a change. Nice cup of tea. Armpits honk a bit. Sam hasn't texted, think I really hurt him. He doesn't deserve the way I treat him.

No sound from Mikey. Why should he call? He's married. He's not in this for the chase. He thinks I'm here to be taken whenever. No man makes the effort when he knows you're always available.

'At first I was afraid, I was petrified . . .'

Can't believe I actually had the nerve to sing that song to Gloria Gaynor. Poor woman.

She was so lovely, she clapped along, and when I forgot the lyrics about keys and locks and doors she sang them to me.

That guy was dancing tonight like he was shaking two maracas and was desperate for the toilet at the same time.

What is it with men at the dancing? Do they think if they sway and clodhop near enough to you, you'll have sex by osmosis?

Yes, Gloria Gaynor.

Told Gloria all Glaswegian women chant her hit doing a conga across George Square every Saturday night, and she was so chuffed. Said to her it was a woman's 'me song' in Scotland.

'Tell all the girls in Glasgow that I'm asking for them, and tell them thank you,' she'd said.

No Gloria, thank YOU.

3.35am

Hey, I may be on the mend.

Thinking of calling Mikey on the mobile and playing the full recording of 'Going To The Chapel, and We're Gonna Get Married' followed by 'I Will Survive' on his voicemail.

I don't, by the way. He might not see the irony.

The Good, The Bad and the Ugly One-Night Stand

15 September
12.30ish am. Kinda.
'You look like Art Garfunkel.'

I'm slurring.

'You Jewish then?' I insist. I'm a stubborn one.

The taxi driver is chuckling. He's more into the rear-view mirror than Hitchcock.

'I'm not answering that question,' he replies.

'Why? Don't you like Art Garfunkel?'

'It doesn't matter if I'm Jewish or not,' he says.

'Of course it doesn't. I know that. But are you?'

'I really don't want to proceed with this conversation,' says David, whatsisname.

'Look. We're going back to mine to have sex. I'm going to find out if you're Jewish at some point,' I insist.

'That'll be four quid,' says the taxi driver.

7am
Yawn. Never done it to classical music before. Not sure if it means I've experienced a cultured shag. Sir Georg Solti has never conducted an orgasm for me. Think he'd be appalled if he knew.

Handel's *Messiah*! I'm going straight to hell. He wrote it when he believed he had a hotline to God.

Wow.

I'm single, can do what I like.

I suppose even God has a partner in Satan.

I think I'm getting too evil.

Better tidy up s'pose.

Okay, so there's my bra . . . I can see a cowboy boot over there . . . good . . . a stocking over the back of the sofa . . . ripped to fuck . . . fine, got more. Oh no, a red wine stain. Arse.

7.05am

Still looking for my knickers.

7.22am

Where ARE they?

7.30am

Fag. Sigh. Maybe I tossed them into the dirty washing basket. Or even the bin with the condoms.

7.32am

This is ridiculous.

If there's anything to make you feel like a teenager again it's losing your pants. The shock of getting them off leaves you quite dizzy. I thought I'd got past that panic. Actually not being able to find them when you're no longer an amateur is a serious carelessness.

Cushions, under the rug, nope, I've looked there, for goodness sake.

7.35am

Wait a minute. He was lurking about the living room this morning. I actually thought for a moment that he was tidying up . . . he kinda rushed out, murmuring summat about a meeting . . . and . . . I'm sure I left them over there beside the fireplace, because . . . that's it . . . we undressed each other there . . . where it was warm and then he . . . he did! He chucked them over to where the CD player is . . . yes! I remember that, because I focussed on them when he changed over to Kiri Te Kanawa

. . . With the Chicago Symphony Orchestra . . . BASTARD!
No way.

7.36am

He's stolen them, lifted, them, pinched them. I thought I saw
him stuffing something into his pocket, over there! Where they
were, that's where he was standing . . . BASTARD!

They're part of a set, from La Perla.

I don't believe it. He's nicked my knickers!

Sure I teased him about his faith, and still feel a little guilty
about it, and all the time the bugger clears each and every sex
scene clutching a sodden, used gusset, a personal parting gift, as
thieving and as intimate as making off with my scalp.

I wish the thought police would arrest me so I can stop
thinking.

6pm

Chain-smoking. I hate men.

10pm

There it is, my whole life at present. Now. Perhaps things will
never get better, perhaps it will be like this forever.

I'm in a complete circle; from a man who gets his thrills
buying me underwear, to the man who makes a one-night-stand
career out of stealing it.

This may not be the city of the damned, but I'll be damned
if I don't leave it before I am. Okay I take the hint guys, all of
you, out there, with your fibs and your kleptomania, I AM
GOING! And I am not coming back, d'you hear me?

22 September

On *Jeremy Vine* today talking about the oppression of women in Islam.

Doing my British female Muslim bit.

I am saying Islam does not condone the subjugation of women, that it is male interpretation of the religion that is responsible for any sexism.

Discover I've yet to convert to Islam. It just doesn't agree with my lifestyle.

Am going to get a T-shirt made saying 'Muslim girls do it better' and wear it on *Richard and Judy*.

3 October

Today I realise I've been around the block. In fact I've been pounding so hard that the block is no longer standing. Historic Scotland is erecting cones and tape around it now, preserving it as a crumbling site of national significance.

Kelvin called today, asking me what I was wearing under my suit. Not sure whether I'm in a position of power with him, or employed by him. Decide that a man with the money you want a slice of is the one who is ultimately in control. As long as you keep him happy he pays. This is not a feminist stance.

Still. Realise that mostly men offer themselves to me and then I take my pick. I'm proud of how professional I must seem. I think. And I can always dump them when I feel like it.

7 October

In a fast black downtown with Heidi.

'George Square please,' I'm asking the driver.

'Well,' he's turning round. 'Was he Jewish?'

'Pardon?'

'Art Garfunkel.'

What? Aha! I'll be . . . ! No way! It's the same damn driver.

'Well . . . was he Jewish?' He's laughing, albeit kindly.

'Yeah, he was, actually,' I'm answering. I'm actually engaging with this, and think it's funny.

'Ha ha ha,' says the driver. 'Was he any good?'

'Oh my God,' cries Heidi. 'Anvar this is too much.'

8 October

12 noon

Awake. Hate being awake. Especially when your mind drifts and you remember. Yes. Just recalled the cab incident. I was chatting away happily to the cab driver who seems to feel he is very well acquainted with my sex life, and who, I feel, supports me in my adventures, if only for the comedy value.

Think I have got to leave town.

10 November

I always try to be honest with myself.

Realise I want to write, drink and shag men, and that I am fast running out of chances in Glasgow to do this. Decide this current crisis is a matter of geography and not one of indiscriminate fucking.

I feel real love won't come my way, ever, not to me, no. Why not just shag and be damned?

Okay, sure, I can renounce my wicked ways and have 'relationships' instead. Decide I'd rather go down South.

15 November

It's all arranged. I'm outta here.

Feel like I'm quitting and feel like a traitor but something tells me that the kind of man I want and the career I crave is far, far from here.

Somewhere, sometime, Sam, Mikey and Art Garfunkel will be history. The whole point about making mistakes is that you leave them behind.

London. LONDON! I hope you can offer me a bigger living than I have. A life that is, well, just a little bit more ME.

17 November

3pm

Heidi's on the phone. Slightly tearful.

'You're doing the right thing,' she says.

'It's okay, you can come down, we'll go clubbing. Nothing has changed.' I'm reassuring her.

'Everything has changed. You are making a break for it.'

Am I in Alcatraz?

Heidi's still blubbering.

'You're going down when you're still a babe. That's good. I'm too old now, to make a break for it.'

'Oh Heidi.'

'You are so brave Anvar. Good luck. I wish I could come with you.'

I'm on my way, taking other peoples' dreams of a wilder, more colourful existence along with me.

22 November

6.30pm

On a train, we've sped past Dunbar, Peterborough. I'm gone, actually gone. Rented a little scabby flat off City Rd N1. £180pw. Feels like a funeral parlour. All dark wood and no natural light. Walking in there is like becoming one of the 'disappeared'. The settee mattress has a large grease stain on the top where Mr Brylcreem boy must have sat watching the TV, all day and all night, lonely and underemployed. Big spiders 'n' all.

Done a runner from my own country. And I can't go back, except for holidays and Christmas. And maybe New Year. And then there's always family birthdays . . .

26 November
7.30pm
Kingston upon Thames, Greater London.

Haven't seen Rhona for two years. Been looking forward to our girlie night for weeks. We grew up together.

Eating pizza in a cafe outside the front door of her duplex while she talks about her exes, one of whom is her husband.

'My love life's very complex, very complicated, very carnal and very consuming,' she's telling me.

Rhona checks her mobile all the time. I think her love life is very capacious too, which I would expect from a girl who is so capricious.

Rhona sure seems to be expecting calls. It's annoying me. I'm feeling angry. Beginning to realise men are given a lot of importance in a woman's life. And I've been guilty of that. How annoying that must be to my mates. We are men-obsessed and judging by their actions men don't seem to give us a second thought. Their first thought is how to get us into the sack. After that nothing much occupies their minds.

8pm
When we're being built, constructed and kick-started into life in the womb, we are just a hotwiring bundle of chromosomes. I'm thinking about this. Well, Rhona is on another call.

We all begin as X-chromosomes and men develop from that, into a Y-chromosome. Says it all really.

8.05pm

Rhona is still talking. Seems the caller doesn't like her attitude; she's looking puzzled and upset.

Remember Rhona, ours is not to question Y.

8.15pm

Guzzling wine. Rhona keeps flicking her eyes nervously over her moby, as if she's waiting for a call from A&E.

Think she should care more about seeing me. Tell her I haven't come over from Islington to watch her getting edgy about who's supposed to call and who doesn't.

'Can't we just forget about men for one night?' I'm pleading like a schoolgirl with a lesbian crush. She's looking at me as if it's the most unreasonable and most unrealistic request she's ever heard.

I'm in ring tone hell. I think I can hear Bohemian Rhapsody by Queen. 'Bismillah. No, we will not let you go! Go, go, go, go . . .'

She's jerking like she's on ECT.

'It's a text!'

8.25pm

I am a moody bitch. Must try to be supportive. Just cos' I'm without love doesn't mean I should be pissed off at a friend who has more choices than she needs.

Mmm . . . Molton Brown handwash and hand lotion. Shit, I'm looking peaky. All the commuting I s'pose. Is she still on the damn moby? Yep, I can see her through the porthole. She's all hunched up and giggling. She's assuming the foetal position over that phone. Bloody hell. Women have a lot more in common than just men.

8.28pm

Feel really left out. Feel that men and women must have a

romantic connection I haven't felt yet.

Can't hang around in the loos all night, waiting for her to hang up. Going back in.

8.29pm
Not that I'm bored counting the minutes she's on the blower.

8.32pm
Rhona's flustered. Tears in her eyes.

'That was, that was . . . he texted, I called him back . . .'

'Take your time.'

God this is tedious. Why can't she just hate men like I am starting to do? I mean. Has anyone asked what they are for?

Poor woman. Maybe her love life really is a mess and she's suffering for it.

Another bottle.

8.40pm
Rhona's still trying to compose herself. It's like watching Madame Tussaud mould a face from wax so that it doesn't end up looking like *The Scream*.

'The man that just texted, well, he's the reason I left my marriage.'

I'm raising my eyebrow. I'm too disappointed to speak.

'We used to meet for lunch once a week, over a long period of time, years, and I knew I loved him.'

'Really?' I'm interested now.

'We never kissed, we never even had sex, but I knew that if I felt like that for him, what I had with my husband wasn't enough.'

Shite. This news is really rocking my world.

I am gobsmacked by the possibility of falling for a guy you haven't even shagged. No, that can't happen, no way. Nigh impossible. And dangerous, I imagine, because if it were true we'd be continually falling for everybody we haven't shagged.

That's a lot of people, in most cases – except mine, of course.

8.45pm

My needy pal is really shaken.

'Rhona, how can you love a man you've never had sex with? It doesn't make sense. I mean, what if he comes too quickly?'

Rhona stops snuffling and is looking at me hard.

'You've got to see the bigger picture, Rhona sweetie. So he comes too quickly, so, every time you mention it he gets all huffy and hurt, and so sex becomes an issue in the relationship, and say, you want to make it better, and want to go to counselling, and he refuses, that will make your relationship even more frustrated and resentment will seep in. Rhona, don't you realise that sex can fuck up a loving relationship?'

'It can't if you don't have any,' she retorts.

Oh.

9.45pm

In a pub. We are drunk. Rhona checks her mobile again. Don't want to upset her but need to know why man of her dreams didn't drag her into the sack.

'RHONA?'

'Ah huh?'

Ninth glass of wine each by the way.

'Why didn't he ask you to sleep with him, your man? I mean, didn't you ever think about the possibility that he may be gay?'

Rhona has a distant look. Shrugs.

'He's married – wife and two kids. She's a bitch. Just shouts at the kids all day.'

Mental note: no more married men, for any of us, they fuck you up.

Am thinking that all those married men out there on the pull either use single women for emotional support or for sex. Lucky for them we have a lot of time on our hands.

'Men don't leave a relationship when there's kids involved,' I say.

We stand here, nodding sagely together.

I really feel for Rhona now.

29 November
2.45pm

Got a ring tone that sounds like a suburban doorbell, like a stranger at the door in a bad play, like an unexpected visitor in a Hammer House of Horror production.

Oh, a text.

> Sorry 2 hear you have left 4 london. hope it wasn't anything i did or said. stay in touch sam xxx

Am I living in the Wild West where women leave town because of a man? Throw our trunks onto a wagon and giddy-up! Running away from the tumbleweed in our hearts?

Jesus, does he really think I'd leave my own country because I may be sulking about some vague sexual misdemeanour?

Jesus, I'm just not that deep. No. I amn't.

7 December
6.45pm

Mikey's name is flashing at me.

Just as well I always keep the numbers of men I'm dating, or have had sex with, in my moby. Just can't get over how important it is to do so. If you don't keep their numbers, they ring and you don't have the choice to ignore the call, and end up having to speak to one of the fuckers.

PRETTY WILD

8.22pm

Ramone is on the moby.

'We MUST go OUT, darling. New bar opening in Hoxton. Very trendy and up and co-ming! Near the Saatchi gallery. Gwen Stefani is expected. Hate her hair, love her lipstick. You on?'

8.32pm

Mikey's still ringing.

Typical. Guys can't take the fact you don't want them anymore. A man is like a boomerang, you throw him away, he comes back.

He's still ringing.

Think men have a gene that means they can take being kept waiting, but not ever being ignored. Bit like a call, and a ring tone then.

Still ringing.

Deep breath. Exhale. Pick up.

'Hey, Mikey, how are you, long time no see/speak?' I am cool, I am casual, I sound confident and au fait with the phone.

'I'm okay, how are you?' He sounds calm.

'Absolutely fine. Really good actually. TV projects on the go, such a buzz down here, it's a very creative period for me I feel.'

'Great. Really pleased for you Anvar. Sounds as if you're happy.'

'I am, yeah, why shouldn't I be?'

I notice I'm pouting.

'Good stuff. Anyway, just a quickie to check in and wish you luck with your new life.'

'Right. Thanks Mikey. That's very decent of you.'

My God, he's being nice about it being over. Does that mean he has somebody else on the side now?

Great. Poor mare. He should come with a health warning. Causes premature ageing. Gives you cancer. Pity there's no hotline number to buzz to help me get over him. How fabulous that'd be; a helpline to help you get over bastards you are addicted to. Freephone Anvar. You Khan Do It.

Huh. Shouldn't have answered. The things you learn, like mistaking geographical distance for emotional detachment.

8.45pm

In the mood for fun, definitely need to feel some other way than numb. Call a stand-by shag. It's the only way.

'Patrick? Hi, it's Anvar.'

'Hey babe, what's up?'

'You in Hoxton tonight? Free tickets to a new bar, free drink, Smirnoff is sponsoring.'

'Sure thing, babe, sounds neat. In Camden right now, getting my head shaved, call you when I get to the Square.'

10.29pm

Ooops, text from Patrick saying he's here, outside somewhere. Get Ramone to go out to find him. I'm in a queue of a hundred for a drink. I mean I'm busy.

'What's he look like, this ma-an of yours?'

'Ramone, you can't miss him. He's black, six foot four, handsome, muscular, might be wearing a basey.'

'Ooooh, might keep him for myself.'

'Ramone just go! I need a shag.'

'Don't we all, love.'

10.35pm

Quadruple vodka. Where is Ramone? Oh, there he is. But . . . who the hell is that guy with him?

'Hi Anvar, how ya doin'? Nice boa.'

'I'm very well, how are you?'

I'm thinking, who IS he? Where's Patrick?

'Swell, swell, let me get you a drink.' This guy's charming.

And on the ball.

'Very kind thank you. Mine's a quadruple vodka.'

Ramone's looking smug. I don't believe this.

I'm stunned. I mean, the guy looks like Patrick, at least.

Ramone has gone all twee and girlish and is faffing with his pearls in excitement.

'Anvar, he's LOVELY! Where did you find him?'

'Ramone, where did YOU find him?' I'm asking.

'Huh?'

'Ramone, honey.'

Shit, how can I put this. I mean, Ramone braved the rain to go find the guy. I mean, I should know better. Do the job myself. It's not Ramone's fault, it's not this guy's fault. I know free vodka runs out and the supply of men never will.

'Ramone, he's the WRONG guy!'

'Huh?'

'Ramone, that guy over there, he isn't Patrick!'

Ramone turns to look at, well, whoever, who smiles back at us.

'Well Anvar,' Ramone is defensive. Like Kenneth Williams being accused of being straight.

'How would you know whether he's Patrick or not, I mean, how many times have you dated anyone, I'm amazed you can remember anyone's face. Ask him to show you his arse and it may trigger something.'

It's an idea.

'He's not Patrick, Ramone. That guy has hair. Patrick got his head shaved today, that's why he might have been wearing a fucking baseball cap and probably still is!'

'But Anvar!' Ramone is genuinely shocked. 'I didn't know he isn't Patrick. What was I supposed to do, I was in an awkward position.'

'Ramone, you're used to awkward positions, it's what your sex life is all about. More tantrum sex than tantric sex.'

'But Anvar,' Ramone is trying to explain the unbelievable. 'That guy, whoever he is, I thought he was Patrick!'

'Why did you think that Ramone?'

'Well.' Ramone is going all coy, and fluttering his eyelashes at, er, our interloper.

'He WAVED at me!'

8 December
5.15am

At least Ramone got a lumber. He says he's going to quit searching Gaydar and just hang out with me.

10 December
4pm

Beginning to adjust to London. Enjoying my anonymity.

London is shag central. People sleep around so much it's impossible to get an appointment at the genito-urinary clinic. So they say.

It's a matter of human traffic. The arteries of London buzz with five million commuters and it is a fact that you will never see the same person twice. This is an absolute boon to all those who have no intention of doing so anyway.

5pm

Don't mean to sound harsh. Suspect I may be somewhat slutty, but I can live with it.

15 December
10.45am

Actually. Come to think of it, it might be quite nice to date again. Been a long time.

3pm

Definitely would be nice to do things like have dinner or go to the cinema. It's all drink, drink, drink and sex, sex, sex. I mean, I'm knackered.

7.05pm

Running myself a bath. Still on the theme of my general whoredom. Realise I've clocked up seven one night stands since leaving Glasgow. Checking my face for signs of guilt or shame. Nope, none.

Hold on. I see creases from the outside of my nostrils down to the corners of my mouth. Aaaarrgghh! Blow job lines if ever I saw them.

18 December

9am

In the edit suite. Again.

My director Nuala is brimming with fulfilment after meeting the man of her dreams in the personal ads. She reeks of contentment. In fact she's positively evangelical about her good fortune.

Don't want to hear it.

I know what to do with sex; I can have it with friends, a lover, an acquaintance, a stranger, and still enjoy it. I think this means I'm on top of my game, so to speak.

Nuala, fresh from a night spent cuddling, feels sorry for me.

She tells me I'm worth more than a one-night stand. Decide everyone else is more bothered about my dirty, single state than I am.

I tell her I don't want a relationship with any of the men I fuck.

Tell her just because I'm single doesn't mean I should be celibate. Can't bear the thought people think I'm being used.

Don't get why women can't do extreme shagging; guys would if only they had the same chance of pulling as a flirty girl like me. There is a reason why men call scoring 'getting lucky'. It's because when we give them the nod, they are chosen.

If I, as a woman, can have as much sport sex as possible and not wilt about the next day waiting for a call, if I can separate my feelings from sex, and not become involved, well, I can have all the fun without the angst. Just like a fortunate man. Don't they get that?

3pm
Nuala calls and says she's sent me an email that she thinks I should read more than once. Send/Receive . . . oh, here it is.

> A, you are smart, funny and never scared to say what you think, even I may add, when this is not appropriate.
> However, you deserve a man who will love you, respect you, and take care of you. You need love.
> I never imagined I could fall in love and now I'm getting married. It's wonderful!
> My friend wrote a personal ad too and met a guy who has just whisked her off to New York! And he's a millionaire!
> Just think about what you really want. Dig deep inside. Be sincere. Be brave. Write it down and see what happens! Look what happened to me!
>
> L, N hugs and kisses

3.01pm
Think I'm going to throw up.

3.02pm
Dunno whether my self-indulgent lifestyle is disgusting me, or the fact there are other women who actually get on with men

to the extent they want to be with one forever. Can't decide which is worse.

3.03pm
Decide women who fall in love experience a lobotomy.

20 December
2pm
Not going home for Christmas. Have to work on TV proposals for next round of commissions. Got to write up at least five of my ideas. Remind myself why I came down South; to get laid, to get rich and to get famous. Should have been a rock star. My rendition of 'Up Where We Belong' is really rather good.

6pm
Stock up on booze, fags and freezer food. Supermarkets down here always look as if there's been a riot. Got the mentality of a war correspondent in the wrong career. I know there's life out there but feel under siege and would rather hide.

7.20pm
Sighing a lot. Thinking about friends I left behind. Wonder how they are. Partying probably. Think briefly about having my own do, but realise my flat's too small to take anyone who can't do a Mrs Pepperpot or an Alice in Wonderland.

9.38pm
Might as well have a drink then.

9.42pm
Feeling a bit low actually.

10.55pm

Goodbye cruel world.

11.18pm

It's Kelvin! Fuck! Blast from the past or what?

11.34pm

Yes, Kelvin, I still have all the underwear you bought me. Do I have it on? No, I don't. It's in a drawer. No, that doesn't mean I'm naked. Are you? No, don't get it out.

Look, Kelvin, really nice to hear from you but I'm going to bed. Yes, alone. Can you talk to me when I'm in bed? S'pose. Not going yet, having another drink. Oh, red wine. No bubbles, no. The rent's too high to buy any.

Did I hear a zip? Kelvin, what are you doing? No, I'm not going to put on the Kenzo thong to please you.

Who's Excalibur?

Put him away Kelvin. You'll have a heart attack.

You want to know when was the last time I wore the purple silk? Oh fuck Kelvin, when I was cleaning, dancing around my kitchen, in the nude, with a feather duster in my hand singing 'I'm So Pretty! Oh So Pretty!'

No, I don't think of you when I put it on. No, Kelvin. No, I'm not going to send you a pair I've worn all day.

I'm hanging up Kelvin.

21 December
12.40am

Wow, I'm officially a masturbatory fantasy. How many men, I wonder, watch us in a queue, or glance at us when we negotiate a zebra crossing and file us away as a snapshot image to be pulled out like a dirty mag centrefold.

Kelvin's generosity, well, there's no such thing as a free munch, in my book. Still can't work out why I accepted his gifts when I can buy them on my own credit card.

Okay, I was puggled.

I think I did it to punish him, take the piss out of him, the way that drink does to me when I'm running to the loo.

Just can't relate to men. Odd creatures. Angry at them. This could be normal. Perhaps men and women are angry at each other all the time. Maybe that's what sex is, a weapon of mass distraction. Stops us killing each other in the war of the sexes. I mean, it's difficult to shoot someone you want to fuck, right? And taking out the whole beastly sex would mean you would never have sex with a man again. You wouldn't want to do that, no.

Not while a man's a great dinner; a meathead with a couple of delicate vegetables in his pants.

25 December – Christmas Day
12 noon

Christmas texts from Glasgow pals, full of exclamation marks, kisses, best wishes and all-round happiness!!!!!

A serious call from the parents. Keep asking me if I'm okay and if I'm eating properly and if I'm coming back home.

I keep saying I've left the country, not you. No one's convinced.

No cards from anyone save one from my radio and TV agents. They are my newest friends. No wonder people in London are lonely.

My choice to be here I guess. Feel like a spare turkey. How appropriate.

31 December
11.59pm

Bottle of cava. Texting everyone in my moby with New Year greetings. Think I should be putting the Hog into Hogmanay instead of sitting home alone.

4 January 2004
11am

The speed-dating craze is getting bigger in London. I think I'd be good at it. 'And the winner of this year's speed-dating championship is . . . Khan . . . clocking up over 567 dates!'

See an ad in the *Evening Standard*. Call the hotline, book a ticket. Pal Jacqui calls from Bearsden, Glasgow.

'Anvar, it's speed dating not speed shagging.'

Everyone thinks I have no intention of slowing down at all. I mean, I can change.

Fridge Magnet Philosophy:
I don't know how many women it'd take to change a light bulb, a long time maybe, because we always want to do it in the dark.

11 January
7 for 7.30pm

No-smoking rule. Apparently putting a cigarette between you and your speed date is rude. When you light up you are guarding your personal space.

I gather when you are a speed dater, you lose certain human rights; namely those of privacy, self-expression and the liberty to make the wrong choice. Being here is about looking at options that are good for you, so you can make the right, sensible decision. Here you are making the right lite choice, from the latest tasty, lean and satisfying range of men, like you would entertain a new diet or exercise plan.

That, and we are being shepherded to the slaughter by health nazis.

I want orgasmic not organic.

Think the rule is short-sighted. Fuck smoking. We are here because trying to find a mate in London is making us mental.

8pm

Got a seat near the door and the toilet. Handy. Room seems full of spectacularly dull specimens, checking their notes with a trainspotter's lust for detail.

Head teacher and Brown Owl are explaining more rules. Tick yes or no beside each person's number. Yes, if you want to see them again, no, if you don't and maybe, if you can't yet decide. Genius. And then hand your sheets back at the end of the night, the way some of us put them into the wash the morning after.

8.01pm

Feeling slightly self-conscious. I'm in a room full of men and women who have given up on the idea of 'destiny', and who have adopted the word 'pro-active' instead.

Dress this club up as a common-sense means of getting a partner all you will, but the heart of the matter is that we haven't found 'the one'. Nay, just about 47 'ones'.

And what's worse, we don't think we will find Mr Soulmate without signing paperwork and paying a fee.

Brown Owl rings a hand-held bell to illustrate the sound that means we must move on to another table.

8.02pm

Course, the essence of speed dating is making your mind up quickly. Don't get long with each other then.

First time I've been with a three-minute man myself.
I'm sighing. Sigh. Sigh. Sigh. I'm sure I look disinterested.
Oh! Red Bull's kicking in. Marvellous.

8.03pm

Worry that if there is such a thing as fate, no one in here is giving it a chance. They all think what's for them has really gone by them. In fact, what was for them didn't even notice them. Didn't stop to say 'Hi!'.

Och, this is useless. You could fill in years with people you are just desperate to like and fancy you, and it's all a waste.

These people do not like being single. They come here as failures, because Venus, the Goddess of Love has not been kind.

Jeez, the damage Relate could do in here.

8.04pm

I'm number 23. It says so on my badge.

Dunno why Quasimodo over there is staring at my breasts and squinting. Shit, he's checking his bit of paper. This is supposed to be a more dignified way of finding a date but it's just a mutton market for metrosexuals.

Oh! The bell's gone, and we're off. It's one of those clinky clanky hand-held numbers that herald the end of school break time.

8.05pm

Warned we have to keep questions short.

WOMEN:	WHAT DO YOU DO FOR A LIVING?
MEN:	DO YOU HAVE SEX ON A FIRST DATE?
WOMEN:	DO YOU LIKE CHILDREN?
MEN:	HOW DO YOU FEEL ABOUT THREESOMES?
WOMEN:	I'D LIKE TO BE ABLE TO GIVE UP WORK TO START A

FAMILY, COULD YOU AFFORD IT?
MEN: HOW OFTEN DO YOU EXPECT A GUY TO WASH?

Okay, okay, so that's what I imagine will go on. The truth, I'm sure, will be much more heavily disguised and difficult to recognise, like, say, what you buy at the end of a night on a piece of pitta bread covered in sauce.

8.06pm (by my watch)
And we're off.

Number 43
Open-neck shirt in white Egyptian cotton, khaki trousers. Smart casual. Handsome. German.
'I'm Jeremy, how iz you?'
'Anvar. Pleased to meet you,' I say, smiling sweetly.
'Sorry, pardon, what, ezcuse me?'
'Anvar. How are you?' I'm asking.
'Zis eez very noisy in here. Can't you say that again?'
'ANVAR!'
'Anzwar. Ah! You are French!'
'ANVAR!'
'Ah! I am Jerzmy. From Germany. I am German you know. Anzwar, very good name.'

Ting-a-ling-a-ling!

Number 14
Surf gear. A bleached beach bum, Australian.
'Cool, here for the giggle, you know. How's you?' he's saying, nervously.
'Fine, yeah, can't do this sort of thing seriously, can you?' I'm being terribly nice.
'Yeah, what's your title babe?'

'Anvar. Ms.'
'Say, what?'
'Anvar.'
'Didn't catch that . . .'
'ANVAR!'
'Ri-ight. Most excellent, Ann.'
'No, it's A – aah, N – nn, V – vee, A – aay, R – arrr.'
'Hey, calm down, no need to be so assertive. I hear you! It's a bit of a weird name but hey, it's cool to be different, right?'
'Yes, so they say.'
'What does your name mean then?'

Ting-a-ling-a-ling!

Number 21

Bespectacled. Jeans. Has put Sun-in on his hair. Rugged. Looks like a presenter on the Discovery channel, the outdoor type who goes chasing twisters. English.
'Don't do this thing often,' he's saying. Course not.
'No, first time for me.' Well, I'm not lying.
'Just for a laugh really.'
'Oh, I KNOW the feeling.' I'm being reassuring again. Typical woman. Always wanting to make everyone feel better, and often at a personal cost.
'Who are you?'
'My name is Anvar.'
'That's unusual. What is it again?'
'ANVAR! My name is ANVAR!'
'Did you just make that up?'

Ting-a-ling-a-ling!

Number 4

Suit. Sleazy smile. In the property business. Apparently. South African.

'Never heard a name like that before,' he's saying. 'Where's it from?'

Ting-a-ling-a-ling!

Notice a woman who hasn't got a man sitting opposite her. She looks really embarrassed and goes to the ladies. How crap is that? When you are stood up on a speed dating night!

Number 11

Chinos. Salesman. Owns a yacht in Kent. Keeps fiddling with his earlobe.

'Anvar? How do you spell that? Exactly?'

Ting-a-ling-a-ling!

There's no way I can get a date when we can't get past the issue of my name. Their illiteracy is preventing me asking the more serious question of myself of whether I could face seeing them again over dinner.

Time for a different approach.

Number 2

Male. That's all I notice. It's enough.

'Hi! I'm Anvar. But hey, you know, call me what you feel comfortable with.'

Ting-a-ling-a-ling!

ANVAR KHAN

Number 7

Male. Fat. Got a lisp.

'Hi, I'm called 'A'. Just 'A'. That's the first letter of the alphabet to you.

'Sit down! I'm 36, single, a cancerian, very independent and I'm looking for a cool guy to go salsa dancing with at weekends!'

Ting-a-ling-a-ling!

Number 13

Hasn't washed his hair.

'Hi, I'm Anvar, take a seat, don't be shy! That's A-N-V-A-R. A! for Amazing! N! N for, er . . . knockout! V! For Vivacious! A! A for A list! R! R for Raring to go!'

Ting-a-ling-a-ling!

Number 1

He takes one look at me and ticks 'no'.

Number 17

It's all a blur of ties and bad haircuts.

Number 20

'Hi! I'm Anvar, but it doesn't matter who I am, because I take personal responsibility for ALL my orgasms.'

Ting-a-ling-a-ling!

9.37pm

I need a drink.

13 January
9pm

Dinner party in Islington. Pal Laura is wafting around the kitchen like Pollyanna. Sitting opposite a Professor and a man and wife who have the same haircuts.

'Did you use a bowl?' asks The Prof.

I like him.

12 midnight

Email tells me my speed-dating result. Outcome: I get two maybes and three yeses. No odds are given on who got my name right.

The Prof asked for my number, by the way.

12.03am

Figure the reason I like no-strings sex is because no one is worth having around longer than a few hours.

Cup of hot chocolate. Bit of bread. Just realising what I'm thinking, about no one being that interesting to me.

That's actually very sad.

12.07am

Bit horny tho'. Think I'll go to bed, lie down and play with my vibrator. It's in the loo. Gave it a bit of a rinse the other day. Right. A bit of DIY Anvar and you'll have a great sleep.

Aahh. Legs open. And relax. Right. What scenario will I choose tonight? I'm in the changing rooms in a swanky lingerie boutique, and my man is in there with me, slipping his fingers down the front of a pair of lacey pants I may buy, and he's asking me if they feel comfortable, as he pulls out the elastic of my gusset and begins to stroke my wet . . . aaarrrgghh! No! Get out of my head! You fucker! No, go away. AWAY! Ruined it. It's not working. There is no room for gatecrashers in my Top Ten turn-on moments.

Get out! Oh no, I can see his face. This is not good. Kelvin you have no place in this fantasy. Bugger off.

Right. Will just go for the vibrating stimulation. That'll get me going. Just lie here and think of a brick wall or summat. Can't be arsed.

What's going on? Oh shit, it's not working. Oh no, I'm really comfortable and everything. It's zizzing like a dying bluebottle. The batteries are low. Using this would be like shagging a man with brewer's droop who doesn't know where your clitoris is.

Shit, don't have any spares. Why are they always AA size like your first bra?

That's it. This is impossible. Will have to get up.

Right. I either check out the vegetable compartment in the fridge or . . . it's finger puppet time. Wait a minute. Ha! Aha! Yes! Rock 'n' roll.

Now where is it? Where's my micro-cassette recorder, such a waste of money. I mean, why tape a thought? If it's such a great line you should remember it. Really like the fact my memory does its own editing job. No, I flatter myself.

Vodka has ransacked my mind and made off with all the good stuff.

And now the TV remote control, yep, the Gods are smiling, and now I need to find a chair. Bit shoogley. How would I explain that at the hospital? Yes, doctor, I was looking for spare batteries for my Rampant Rabbit, the Deluxe version you know, I mean, I don't skimp on the important things, and I just fell off the chair! Just like that! Why was I balancing on a swivel chair? Er, because I was trying to reach the smoke alarm.

Voila! Aha! Excellent result. Now have a selection of batteries to work with.

1.15am

Phew. Nice one. Think I should replace the smoke alarm batteries. Change my mind. Decide having an emergency orgasm rather than a working emergency alarm is more of priority.

Rampant Rabbits are cool, but never quite know what to do with the ears that are stuck on the side of the vibrator, like a thumb is to your first finger.

Up your ass, maybe, or clasping your little love button, dunno. The gears are good tho', get you there as fast as you can say Bugs Bunny.

What's Up Doc? Nothing when you have a Dr Love toy handy. They could launch one called 'What's Up Cock?' as the more male-friendly version.

14 January
11.05pm
Online. Have received emails from my three yeses from the speed dating trial.

From: Jeremy
Sent: January 14, 12.36
To: glasgowgirl@popupjock.com
Subject: Re:
Hi! Anzwar/Anzvar (it is this, yes, it is not?) yep, a very enjoyable evening, and chat, and yez, I am thinking, why not? Let us meet. Call me.

From: Surfboy
Sent: January 14, 14.21
To: glasgowgirl@popupjock.com
Subject: How ya doin?
Ann Var, Hi! Am outta town until weekend so wanna go out after? On skateboarding weekend next week so cool soon as? Shane.

From: Nigel
Sent: January 14, 15.03
To: glasgowgirl@popupjock.com
Subject: Drinks
Dear Annie, lovely to meet. Am in London next week so
if you are interested in meeting me (again!!!) bounce back
a reply at this email address or, if you prefer, please call me
on my business number.
Regards, Nigel Stanisklowski.

12.05am
Oooooh, so many men, so little time.

16 January
1.32pm
The Prof calls, asks me to a classical music concert. Not sure
what to wear. Settle on hot pants and a leather jacket.

5.45pm
The Prof is looking at me as dismissively as a dead fish on my
plate, one that knows it is dead but is bored with the afterlife
already.

5.46pm
Really wish I'd chosen something conservative in, say, jersey or
cashmere, and full length. Don't think he likes me anymore.

7.45pm
Beautiful! Love it! Chopin is gorgeous! Feel so relaxed, like my
whole consciousness has been massaged.
    'Hey Harry Handsome! Chopin has really kick-started my Chi.'
    I think he's smiling, his lips are pursing, that's all I have to go
on. Decide to go for a glass of wine somewhere sedate, I guess.

8.01pm
The moby's off! Oh no, it's Kelvin.

Ignore it. No use. Avoiding taking a call on a date looks really dodgy. It's off again. How embarrassing. Don't recognise that number. Glasgow? Who could that be? Switch it off. Explain to the Prof that the calls are business and I'll get them later.

8.48pm
'And then my wife had an affair.'

The Prof seems to be quite a sad man.

'Couldn't you have had counselling?' I'm asking, wondering why if anyone is lucky enough to find true love they can give up that easily. I mean, sex is just sex, isn't it?

'No, I divorced her.'

'Oh, I see, I'm sorry.'

'Nope, no need. That was it. No questions, no arguments, no big emotional scenes. Over.'

'Well, I suppose it's very difficult to recover from, a blow like that . . .' I'm trying to be sympathetic.

'Are you good with children?' he's asking. Is this a fucking speed date?

'My children are my biggest and only tie, you know.'

I see.

'Erm . . . well, I don't have any, but I have friends who are, you know, married, sorry to mention that, again, and they have kids.'

'Do you get on with the children?' he's asking.

'I play hunt the invisible hamster with them.'

'Hunt the invisible hamster?'

'You tell them you've found it and pretend to hold it up by its tail, they disagree with you and point at another room, very difficult game to end.'

The Prof doesn't seem to be staring at me in such a sleepy, piscatorial fashion any longer.

Whatever he was interviewing me about, it seems I've passed.

ANVAR KHAN

9.20pm
Listen to Kelvin's voicemail. 'I need to be a very bad boy. I need to come for Anvar. Can I do that? Can I do that for you? Can you call me back? I'm in the house alone.'

Is this 0898 Anvar?

9.35pm
'Would you like to come back to mine for a cup of Horlicks?' the Prof is asking, eyeing my moby. 'Or do you have something more important to do?'

10pm
In a taxi. Thinking.

Of course Kelvin should be in the house alone, what is he talking about, what does he mean by letting that slip? Arse. He's got a housekeeper or a lodger or, dare I say it, a woman.

Nothing surprises me any more.

Look over at the Prof. He looks as if the world is populated by bad smells. Well. What the hell. At least a divorced man with commitment issues is actually single.

10.02pm
Scrub the two voicemails. Occurs to me suddenly that the other one might not be from Kelvin.

Well, whoever it is, there's no caller ID, so it must be a stranger, or a man, probably, and if I haven't kept his number then he's SO out the picture. Fine. Whatever.

11pm
I suppose I should feel a bit more pissed off. But I don't care about Underwear Man. Figure all men are dishonest. It's like when they want you for sex they presume you know the score, that this is all they have to offer, the equality of being a partner in crime.

Hmmm. It's too cruel.

Wonder if my hussy nature makes them think I'm on their side. A fun girl. A people person. A man's best friend.

Oh Lord! I get it now. What a shocker.

I am rentaslut.com. No Cock Too Small, No Ego Too Big.

There it is, somehow, in Hollywood lights. Or in a sound, or my laugh, or the way I walk – noticed, heard and responded to like a whistle only dogs can hear.

I reek of sex. It's almost that I don't know how else to smell.

So. Right. Got that sussed. Really think I'm onto something with that.

Anyway. I think, sort of, that if I am to go down the route of sexual adventure, to protect myself it is probably better to presume every man who comes on to you is on the make. I think, given on the evidence I have gathered so far, this is only fair.

11.20pm

Really not sure about the Prof. Well, saves me being at home in front of the telly. He's a guy to go out to concerts with; together we could do the whole classical repertoire.

Oh, a glass of champagne, lovely.

'What happened to the Horlicks?'

'That was a joke.' The Prof is definitely a wild card. Thing is, he looks like a Horlicks man.

'Is the vintage champagne okay?' he's asking.

'No. Go on. I'll just have a Tia Maria, thanks,' I'm teasing. Silence.

'That was a joke,' I snigger.

Jeez, bubbles really can make a noise in your glass. Really. I was prepared to make the effort, now I'm just bored.

18 January

12.15am

Text from Sam.

Funny, shagged Sam because I decided our friendship wasn't really going anywhere, and, well, because I could.

Now realise I don't want to lose him as a pal.

Think his text is flagging up personal issues of mine regarding the opposite sex. He likes me and values me, more than having sex with me, and well, that just doesn't seem to correspond. Wonder why? I mean I don't hate my father and I enjoy male company. And I don't think ALL men are scum.

12.48am

I don't believe this. We are arguing the Prof and I. Mr Horlicks is getting his thermals in a twist. I'm a writer, I am familiar with the way words work. Is this anal, or wot?

I'm winning an argument about whether the word 'individuate' exists. This guy went to Oxford, me, I went on the dole.

He's a very intelligent man, but he is in real danger of patronising me here. Oh, he's off to look the word up.

Oh thanks yes! I know I'm right. Get over it mate. Aha, he looks impressed, if not a little outdone.

This is obviously the guy who put dick into the word dictionary.

1am

Back at mine early like a wage slave who has to get up in the morning. If I cut sex out of the equation, like Heidi did with her man, perhaps my romantic career will take a turn for the better.

No sex, no snogging. A peck on the cheek and I let myself out. Think I'm acting like a proper grown-up for once, not rushing into anything.

19 January

3pm

Sitting on the sofa, naked, save a pair of biker boots and a butterfly clip on my hair.

Online.

Email from speed dating trial.

From: Surfboy
Sent: January 19, 13.21
To: glasgowgirl@popupjock.com
Subject: Remember me?
Hey Ann, hi hey how ya doin? Sent you an email, you get it? Man, I'm around and waiting. Doin' ma thing. Shane

S'pose I could see him. He might be the greatest shag in the universe, I mean, you gotta have some compensation for being a fanny.

4pm

Feel like pigging out. Nothing in. Fancy a curry. Where's that takeaway leaflet.

Oh. The landline's off.

'Hi Anvar, it's Frank here.'

Duh?

'Professor Frank Sullivan.'

'Oh, hi, how are you Frank?'

'Just phoning on the off chance you've never been to Brussels?'

'No, never.'

'I'm off for the week. Want to come?'

8pm

How exciting! I mean, this is the way it's supposed to happen. Isn't it? As long as we keep away from any crosswords we'll be fine. Hurrah!

He's sweeping me off my feet! Wow, this could be it! It's all very sudden and romantic. Thank goodness I'm freelance/freelunch journo.

And we'll have sex for the first time too! Maybe Frank's mad in bed. Wonder what it'll be like. I've heard those intellectual types are very dirty in bed, very highly sexed. He might even be, how you zay eet, a bit kinky.

Wish I'd invested in some designer luggage. I mean, if I'd known I'd be jet setting . . .

Wow! Brussels! And Frank has his own apartment there, we'll be over every weekend surely, and my French! How is it nowadays?

Comment ça va? How are you? Je m'appelle Anvar. Et tu? Je suis fatigue. Zut alors! Merde! Croissant. Hmm . . . I'll get a French/English/English/French dictionary.

Oooh! Europe a-go-go . . .

8.10pm

I'm so happy for me! Once I've planned my daily outfits I can relax.

I should maybe update my house dress too. I mean, I'll be hanging out while he's at work. Oh fuck it, a basque is for every occasion. It's not just a separate. I can just throw a shawl over it for breakfast occasions.

20 January
9.30pm

At a dinner party for eight in Hampstead. Have been asked along as a single to make up the numbers because someone is bringing their child. Condescending married fools. No wonder single women stay single; we keep getting asked along to couples events. There's no one to seduce.

No wonder husbands keep hitting on us. We're like innocent wildebeest thrown to the lions. They might not be hungry but even they can't pass up an opportunity.

As I keep being told to keep more of my own counsel, I don't say anything about the Prof. However, quietly chuffed that I've sabotaged the seating plan designed to combat my alleged isolation. I do this by sitting at the top of the table, where I belong.

10pm
Pished.

11.23pm
Pished and accident-prone.

Knock red wine onto the white linen tablecloth. Pour salt onto the stain. Get up to go to the loo catching the tablecloth on my belt buckle. Salt cascades onto floor. Nancy with the eye-tuck slides on the granules in slippers that look like rejects from Aladdin's wardrobe but apparently they're designer originals.

On her arse clutching a quail's egg and a profiterole.

Taken to sit down and catch her breath in the living room. Demonstrate the Highland Fling to lighten the mood.

Corner a woman in the toilet and try to snog her. Surprised when she grabs my breasts. I run out screaming that the hostess is a lesbian.

Light up with the stress and told to smoke on the balcony. Realise the woman I snogged isn't the hostess, who has taken to her bed. Dunno if the other woman is in fact a lesbian. Can't remember which one she was.

Set fire to a shrub I'm using as an ashtray. Cry and tell everyone I'm a nice person.

Crash out. Wake up on my doorstep. Crawl whimpering on all fours to my flat. Sleep in bath.

21 January

11am

Write letters of apology. Feel like sending myself a wreath signalling the end of my life as a heavy drinker. Realise the weird stuff happens to me when I'm sober. On alcohol my life is surprisingly mediocre.

4.08pm

Hate planes. Hate flying. Hate being in the clouds, like being caught up in God's cigar smoke.

5.14pm

Brussels International Airport. Taxi to Ixelles – armed with euros. Wonder if I'm nervous.

6.10pm

Knock door. Prof isn't in. Doesn't have a mobile. Can't call him. Feel panic. I might have got the day wrong. Think hotel. Wait for nearly 30 mins. Door opens, Prof standing in hall. Gives me hug. Tell him the doorbell isn't working. Says he was on phone to daughter and didn't want to let her know he had a female visitor.

8.20pm

In one of the best Chinese restaurants in the world. Prof orders three vegetable dishes.

'I've been veggie for 18 years now,' he's saying. Feeling very chilled and happy, nay almost sophisticated and settled into my new lifestyle.

Tits a bit sore. Expecting a period. Typical.

9pm

I pay. Prof says he's waiting for money to be transferred from his University. Go to cocktail bar. I pay. I am a walking ATM.

PRETTY WILD

11pm

Back at his. Realise we've not yet snogged. Worry that the Prof and me are not being normal. Surely if you are into someone you get on with it? Still, the patio doors are open. Brussels is warm, I'm in Europe! and the Prof is quietly and studiously preparing some herbal tea. Camomile – to help us sleep. He sure isn't giving me any come-on signals.

11.42pm

Oh yes! I'm in! I am in bed. He's in the loo. Not long now.

12.03am

Well, we did have spicy sauces.

12.18am

I can hear gurgling.

12.21am

Even girls don't take this long.

12.22am

Oh, don't mind me when you're busying yourself with your ablutions.

12.23am

Och, at least he's making the effort. Anticipating Colgate-freshened breath. Maybe he's washing his cock. Some women have to chin a man about that sort of thing. Oh, yeah, Julie, the dental assistant, with the cleft palate, she used to make her man clean his before she went down on him.

12.24am

Still lying here luxuriating in fresh linen waiting to be worked into an Imperial Lather.

12.36am

Mustn't nod off. Did I hear a lock click open?

Oh, I can hear celestial trumpets! He's naked. The animal. Fabulous. At last. Slight hair chest. Well defined pecs. Fit bugger. Muscular but not a gym buck. Oh, uh, he's coming over, he's getting near now, he's at the foot of the bed, he's climbing over the footboard, practically throwing himself over like Daley Thomson. Actually, he's not as graceful, I have to say, it's more like watching *It's A Knockout*!

Now. Ooooh. He's looming over me like a table, planting a smacker on my lips and just hovering and smiling at me. Is this what you call sensitive sex?

No, he's placed his hands tight over my wrists. He's still a table, I'd like more of a teapot, you know what I'm saying?

He's not moving. He's still smiling at me. This feels like a yoga exercise.

Oh, here we go. Hmmmm . . . uh . . . uhhuh . . . hmmm . . . at last, a slow, sensual snog. Shit, trying to manoeuvre my body up to his to at least feel some skin-to-skin contact. Nope, he's intent on at least two feet of distance. Yep, he's looking down at my cunt. Oh, I see, he's going to go down on me. Oh yes! No mucking about.

Aaaah. Good. I await a multiple. My eyes are half-closed, my breathing measured and getting deeper . . .

Actually, actually, hold on a minute, that doesn't feel right. What IS he doing?

He's just sticking his tongue in; in and out, in and out, quite robotically. This is minimal-requirement bullshit. Right. Am moving my hips a little to help him hit my moon.

He really needs some help down there.

I'm wet, so it's cool. I mean I had 40 minutes to warm myself up while he was in the toilet. But, at his age, he should know more and perform better.

Oh no, I get it, he's using the 'marriage position' on me, the one that worked for years on his wife, and which he is now committed to using on all women as a sort of tried and tested measure.

Okay, now what's happening? Hard to say really.

The tongue is still. If I remember rightly even allowing for any unusual personal techniques, it should at least be wiggling slightly.

Oh, he's licking. Frantically. Uh, huh, uh, huh, uh, huh, uh . . . My pearl is hardening. Whit? Huh?

Why has he stopped and is looking up at me smiling?

'That'll help you sleep, that was nice wasn't it?'

You are having me on.

12.38am

He's out of it. He's rolled over and is snoring. That will help me sleep? What, a shag that lasts as long as it would take me to pop a couple of nytol tablets?

The Prof goes down on me for less than a minute? You'd only give a person oral sex for such an unreasonable length of time if you were working them up for a full half hour at least.

Okay, Anvar, you're building a relationship, this is not about sex, this affair, it's about being honest and being yourself and getting to know each other.

His previous lover must have been the fastest cum in the West.

22 January
11am

Feel slightly detached today, wandering around this three-storey all on my lonesome. Wouldn't even mind a few emails or texts, well from anyone really.

11.10am

Lord, my period. No wonder I've been feeling floaty.

6pm

I am so BORED! Wish I'd packed my vibrator. Opening a window to smoke. Know the Prof doesn't approve but I DON'T CARE!

6.15pm

Put on Iggy Pop. Loud. 'Now I'm Gonna Be Your Dog'. Rock 'n' fucking roll. I am a woman! And I deserve a man who knows how to turn me on!

6.20pm

Construct a quiz for the Prof. Is a clitoris a) a sea anemone b) a flower c) a girl's name d) all of the above.

Any man who even attempts to answer this will be asked to back away from the bed, slowly and carefully, with his hands up.

6.32pm

Tra la la la la la la la la la la . . .

6.40pm

He's back. Hi! Meeting go okay? Fancy a drink? You've no cash yet! Jeez, bank's a bit slow eh?

No I haven't been to the supermarket.

Oh, you know, just hanging out, doing a bit of writing.

How do you put the heating on?

It's expensive?

No there's no bread, I ate it. And the cheese.

We're going out? Great. I'll change.

Your daughter's coming over from Spain and she's hoping to meet me? Erm . . . right. You sure that's not too early in our, er . . . relationship?

Oh I'm sure we'll get on, don't fret.

Oh yeah, I stained that hand towel, sorry.

PRETTY WILD

6.50pm

So, he's broke again. I agree to pay for the meal. What the hell. I'm here for a while. It'll resolve itself. I've got to give relationships a go. Everyone says you have to work at it. I mean, I can't sleep around forever.

7pm

Hear my mobile go off on the top floor. Ignore it.

9pm

Post dinner. Back at flat. Prof notices open window and stops. He's obsessed. I'm watching him moving the window back and forward, as if he doesn't understand the spring mechanism. Did we order a bottle of loopy juice?

9.28pm

Ablutions time again. Yawn. We're in a bathroom on the upper floor where there is a camp bed and a toilet. He wants to sleep here tonight because he says he likes the dawn-light effect.

Presume he'll go downstairs to the other loo, for, you know, privacy.

9.30pm

Am busying myself brushing my teeth. Doing it slowly, killing time.

Where's he gone? Wonder if the sex will be as lukewarm tonight.

And brush. Oh I can see him in the mirror. He's sitting behind me, he's sitting down . . . where? Am slowly standing up straight, with my brush dangling from my lower jaw and with a mouth full of foam.

Oh! Horror of horrors! He's on the throne. Can't believe this! He's actually on the throne! This is just outrageous!

And he's just sitting there, reading a book!

79

Nightmare! Absolute fucking nightmare!

No, don't turn round Anvar, he'll just be having a pee. He just does it sitting down is all. No need to panic. No need to get upset. Just keep brushing, that's it, keep brushing.

I mean, it'd be plain rude to do anything else, and far too soon. You just don't do this kind of thing, especially with someone you've known less than a fortnight. A pee yes, maybe, but anything else is just out of the question.

Oh God! Don't look in the mirror either. Guys look like really sorry specimens when their trousers are in a crumple around their ankles.

It is the longest pee in the world tho'. A Guinness Book of Records number, if you drank all the Guinness first.

I mean, this is mad. Highly unusual.

Shitting in front of other people is for newborn infants, or women squatting in ploughed and fertile fields that need manure. It's a third-world thing. Or an I-have-just-been-born thing. It's not what people do after they have been out to dinner.

Oh no! NO! I don't get this! I don't know what to do for the best. He's farted. He's actually farted.

9.31pm

Keep brushing, Anvar. No. Gotta stop. He'll know something's up soon. Am scraping the enamel off here.

Oh, Donald Duck noises. NO! It's too horrible! Oh, there's more. Oh no! He's pushing. He's having a shit! I don't believe it!

9.32pm

Am lying in the camp bed, singing to myself quietly. One eye on the loo. Oh, he's reaching for the toilet roll. Aaarrgghh! Can't look! Avert my eyes. Oh, he's stopped, a paragraph has caught his eye. Nope, his hand is at his behind . . . oh this is dastardly.

I'll pretend to be asleep. I've got the cover up to my nose. Don't want to smell anything. Am I supposed to shag him after this? I cannot believe my life, I really can't.

9.34pm
He's washing his hands. Maybe I should be grateful he feels he can be himself in front of me. It takes some couples decades to achieve this kind of intimacy. If you can call it that.

9.42pm
Oh no, he's jumped on the bed like Spiderman. He's smiling at me. Doesn't he realise what he has done and how wrong it is?

Oh, no, not the 'going down' on me spectacular! He's a one trick pony.

Am frigid with apprehension. Keep looking over at the porcelain toilet seat. It's haunting me, staring back at me, triumphant. It's the most mesmerising pan I have ever seen in my puff. I don't think I'll be able sit on one again without going through the trauma of what I saw tonight. A flashback that never fades.

Aha! Got it! I remember, I don't have to go through with this, nope, I can get out of this without mentioning the seriousness of the Armitage Shanks debacle.

'Frank, Frank, I've got something to tell you, it's important, there's one thing you should know.'

That chin is now parallel to my navel.

'I'm going to lick you out.' Seems very chuffed with himself.

'Frank, I've got my period.'

'Oh.' He looks green. He looks confused. Perhaps he doesn't know that women get periods.

'We can still fuck,' I protest. He's not looking well at all.

'I can't do that, I don't do blood, I'm a vegetarian.'

9.43pm
He's insane. He is cuckoo, didn't fly over the nest so much as fall from it and bang his head.

10pm

He's lying beside me, and I think he may be in some sort of petulant mode. He seems quite angry. I know. He won't come near me. Pleased about this. Yet very aggravated by it too.

Don't think he's just a vegetarian, decide he's really a vagitarian. He doesn't do cunt. Full stop.

10.15pm

He's asleep. That was it. No more chat, just complete dismissal. And all this is for what? To sleep in a camp bed?

In a three-storey pad, I'm on a camp bed, in what used to be the servant's quarters? And now I'm raising my voice in my head to sound like an American? I think this is because they are professionals at complaining about consumer items and I feel just as disappointed at myself for buying into a man who has provided me with nothing but bad service.

10.42pm

What time is this to be in bed?

Check mobile, listen to voicemail. Strange voice, bursts of high-pitched shouting, sounds like Klingon, spoken by a Japanese tourist. Wipe it.

Big sigh but no big zeds.

Will buy some Nurofen tomorrow, if I live until then.

11pm

Feeling quite emotional, and let down.

11.10pm

No way I can last here until the date of my return ticket. Mind you. We've been spending so much of my own cash, dunno if I can afford to go home earlier. Like now.

11.35pm

Drift into a snooze. Leg's pounding like a cantering horse. That, or I was a German soldier before my current incarnation.

Wonder that every woman should have a savings account for times she has to escape a situation with a man who has gone from lover to enemy; from friend to madman; from potential partner to someone you don't even like very much.

23 January

8am

Am trying not to be awake. He's on the toilet again. I can hear him farting in the near distance. Go back to sleep. Quickly.

8.15am

I can only look at him with one eye open now.

What the hell is he doing? He's turning the bar of soap. He's turning it so the soggy side is up to dry out.

Thinking of getting in touch with the British Embassy. They'll help me.

8.30am

He's off to a meeting. Left in the flat. Trying to write. Feel very unsexy, very ignored and extremely spaced out. Sniff around his belongings.

Piles of them, in that cluttered mess the intellectual always seem to live in.

Find photos. Pictures tell stories, the real tale, not the one you are told face to face by someone who doesn't realise how transparent a camera makes you.

I know I won't like what I see. I can feel it. I sit down with a glass of water. Here goes.

A blonde, wrinkled, middle-aged woman. Find about a hundred photos of the same blonde, middle-aged woman. A sort of Lana Turner type, left to rot, in a poverty of choice.

In some of them she's posing with a girl who looks like Frank's daughter. Maybe this tired blonde is his wife, maybe his one real love. She probably settled for Frank. Her compromise shows in her stupefied gaze at the camera that perhaps used to burn a hole in the lens.

Flick through several packets of Polaroids. The person who took the pix took at least 20 of her at a time, whether she was just sitting with her knees tucked under her on a couch, or posing in front of the anteater amphitheatre at the zoo.

See enough to know he's still screwed up over someone else.

This makes sense. All of it makes sense. He's looking for a replacement. Anyone really. How degrading for me.

There's a shoebox of receipts on the bottom shelf of a bookcase. Haul it out. Plane tickets, credit card receipts . . . very, very many credit card statements, oh yeah, I mean he's been skint for ages and why then, can't you pay with your card? Damn. I shouldn't be so generous. Shouldn't have forked out all the time.

That figures. I'm rubbing my forehead with the palm of my hand. Letters from his bank demanding payments. This guy's in serious debt.

I am outta here. Running away again, I know. But let's look at the information available; he knows his daughter won't like me and will resent me. He wants a woman who is independent because he needs a woman with money as he hasn't got any. He's emotionally frigid because he's still in love with Blonde Woman.

Which is why he's trying me out as a mate before actually treating me like one.

Dammit, I've been duped again. Get out, Khan.

3pm

All the Belgians like to hang out in cafés drinking coffee and smoking. Do the same.

Feel incredibly isolated. Prof turns up around 5pm. What does he expect? A blow job and a hot bath?

5.30pm
He suggests a concert and then dinner. I say I have no cash. He looks upset, puzzled.

He says we'll have to stay in then.

7.16pm
We haven't spoken since not having dinner.

11pm
Decide I'm not going to hang around for the full fuck. I've never been turned on by mysteriousness. I don't consider a man's reticence to be attractive. It is actually possible to be let down before the build-up.

Ask the Prof to run me to the airport in the morning. Tell him he can enjoy the camp bed. Doesn't even fight back.

When I turn in he switches off all the lights and sits on the stairs in the dark with his head in his hands.

I know he lives with some sense of having fucked up his family life and the guilt of that. But I ain't no fucking nurse, and I ain't no experiment.

I don't want no cripple.

24 January
3pm
On a plane back to London. Have a glass of wine and lust after my life of non-responsibility and cut-throat hedonism. I never valued it before. Now it stands quite correctly and usefully as a privilege.

I'm a lucky girl to be so free, so unreliant, on any man.

Depend on them, and they do as they will with you. You

might be able to trust a guy not to knock you onto the tube track at rush hour, but you could never trust one with your heart, should you, of course, ever take the risk of giving it.

28 January
4pm
'Hi Anvar, it's Nigel!'

It's one of the speed daters.

'Hey, how are you?'

'Fine, just in Manchester, business to sort out you know. On the road, bit noisy.'

'Yes, it's quite a bad line isn't it? What are you up to?'

'Oh, some employee of mine, he's gone awol, trying to track him down.'

'Nigel, that's terrible.'

'Yes, I'm hands-on you know. These people have worked for me for a long time, built up the deep sea diving business, offshore. I feel responsible. Been working the boys too hard.'

'Oh Nigel I hope it works out for you.'

Fuck, I'm impressed, a man who's self-made. Brilliant.

'No worries. Listen Anvar, I'm flying one of my planes this weekend, just an aeronautical show I display at, so can I call you next week?'

'Sure.'

'By the way Anvar,' he's shouting.

'Wot?'

'I like calling you Annie.' For some reason I'm pleased.

7pm
Right, enough is too much already. I figure I need a taste of something different. I think I should see what it's like to be with a man who can be a strong-enough match for me. Nigel it is.

In retrospect, all my boyfriends enjoy the rather lame ambition of just shagging me now and again and staying in the pub. With that as the norm, you can't argue against the need for a change.

8pm

Looking up Nigel on the net. Shit! He's mentioned in connection with a Hollywood blockbuster. Ha! He's a fucking millionaire.

This is the pay-off, this is the absolute reason I have been wasting my energy on no-hopers – it's all a-changing now.

10pm

Pissed. On the phone to mates, telling them I've snagged a guy who may be a 'good prospect'. There really is a Cinderella in all of us girlies. We all have a fairy tale inside us, a script just waiting for a man who comes along and seems to fit the lead role.

11.50pm

Well arsed. Very smug.

Thinking of our first date; a few bottles of Bolly at his expense, an evening of being shown around his gated mansion, admiring objets d'art and his private helipad. Ours is going to be a *Hello!* magazine spread of a relationship.

12.01am

I've really got to get over myself. Still, it's a laugh.

31 January
4.15pm

Moby's off.

'Hey, Anvar! Jezemy here. Thanks you very much for your email. I thought you'd forgotten about me! Ha ha ha. I'd really like to meet wiz u.'

'Yes, Jeremy, hi, er yes, so would I, really, really I would.'

'I feel zat we really got on, on our speed dating.'

'That's very sweet of you to say so. Me too.'

What did he look like again?

'I looked at you and my internal checklist said, yes, I could meet zis girl again.'

Oh dear. To use a modern analogy: he's on Vodaphone, I'm on Orange. We have network problems.

'What's your "internal checklist", exactly?'

'Oh, it's what ze men have, the colour of your eyes, the way you smile, your laugh, your manners, if it all suits . . .'

'I see.' No I don't.

'Why don't we meet in ze Soho tomorrow?'

'Smashing Jeremy.'

'I will call you then, yes?'

Bye.

5pm

A few men on the go, not in love with any one of them, all is as it should be. If they are boring, as they seem to be, then at least there is no danger of me falling for one of them.

5.20pm

Always best to see men you know don't do it for you. It's okay to shag men you don't fancy, that's what drink is for.

6pm

Marks & Spencer creamy pasta and a bottle of chianti. It's important to be nice to yourself. I'm the only person around who can treat Ms Khan this way.

8pm

Decide on a new set of rules; use men for sex only. Dump any stand-by shag after four dates, this prevents you becoming 'involved'. I mean, if you conducted a socio-sexual experiment by asking a woman to sleep with a man regularly you bet she'd be crying after a month or so 'But I love him'.

My way means you enjoy sex but protect yourself from being a square.

Don't let any affair continue for more than three months of seeing each other only once a week. And always date other men. The more men you have the less likely you will be able to distinguish any of their redeeming features, and will therefore find it hard to hanker after a romance with any of them.

I mean you won't have time!

The biggest challenge will be remembering their names.

8.30pm

Yes, I'm back! No man will get to fuck with me now.

1 February

9am

Moby rings. Don't answer. Asleep. Voicemail.

'Anvar, it's Jezemy. Sorry I forgot that I can't see you today. I have to go to church with my family, so will have to postpone our date. Thank you for your understanding. I'll call you later. Hope you aren't too, how you say, inconwenienced.'

I'm awake. Did he say 'church'?

11.59pm

Ding Dong. Oh, a message. Could be exciting. Text from Shane. The Speed Date Surfer.

Ann Var! Wotcha! Wooohooooo!!! Can't wait to see ya baby. Got a big smile on when I got your email. Excellent!

Fridge Magnet Philosophy:
Men, some you miss, some you lose.

2 February
3.20pm

Absolutely shagged after a hard day's shopping in Oxford Street. Scottish *News of the World* called to talk to me, explained I was now in Versace and had to concentrate on what I was trying on.

Think they worry they pay me too much.

5pm

It's the millionaire! Wow, he calls when I'm spending money. Quelle surprise! It's fate. Soon I'll be able to strut down Bond Street dressed casually in diamonds.

'Anvar! Nigel.'

'Hello. How are you?'

'Bit held up at moment. Got to go to Ireland tonight. Over there for a few days. Can you hear me?'

'Yes, just. Line's really rough.'

'Yep, I'm on the road again. Having car trouble too. I don't usually drive the Lamborghini but it's got speed you know? I've clocked up quite a few miles on this thing.'

'Jesus Nigel, you seem to be always on the move.'

'I know, Anvar. My mates call me the Scarlet Pimpernel, they can never get hold of me. I feel really bad about it sometimes.'

'Och don't worry Nigel. You're just doing your job.'

I am so sympathetic towards this guy.

'Yep. Gotta meet with a film company in Dublin you see.'

'I know, I know, you don't need to explain.'

'So I'll call you when I get back to my house in Surrey. Okay?'

Coolio.

10pm

Call Nigel on his mobile. It goes straight onto voicemail. Shame.

3 February

11pm

Take a maddy about the spooky Prof. Recall his phone is two flights down from his bedroom and it's way past his Belgian bedtime. Do a 141 then call his number and let it ring until he answers. He'll think it's one of his children. Hang up.

11.25pm

Repeat.

11.42pm

Repeat.

11.55pm

It's engaged. Smile as I realise he's spending money calling all his relatives in London and in Spain and in Germany, worried, in case there's an emergency.

2.45am

Wake up sweating. Like someone has poured a swimming pool over me. The bed sheets are soaked with the shape of my body, an outline like the chalk around where the murder victim fell.

Strange dream. Out with Nigel.

He keeps saying he wants to relax, and takes out one of his fast cars for a spin, tells me it's an Aston Martin, a car he bought from a Hollywood film director, says it's the same car James Bond picked up his girlies in. I feel really distressed by this.

Think he really prefers blondes, well, that's every brunette's nightmare.

I creep into his high-security carpeted garage with a constant temperature of 18 degrees, and decide that he loves me and trusts me enough to take his Bentley out for a spin.

Dreams are mini-movies with no sense of location.

I'm in a private box, applauding his aeronautical skills at one of the many air shows he organises featuring recycled B52 bombers. He crashes. He dies and comes into my room looking for me and then I realise he's not real, he's a ghost.

4 February
6.35pm

'Jezemy' has met me all the way from Morden. He's pilfered at least seven packets of free alcoholic sweets from a tequila promotions girl and is munching on them madly. He has the teeth of a brontosaurus. I hope we are not going to eat at a buffet because I fear he will scoop portions fit for the whole of Soho onto his plate.

Stop at a sushi bar. He coughs loudly to get the attention of the waiters.

It's fucking self-service.

Aware that manufacturers don't make eggshell carpets, pity, because I feel I'm walking on a very long one.

Noodles, prawns, squares of cold rice and weak wasabi. Try to make chat.

Always talk about the family first.

'What's your mum like?' I venture. Hey, smart question, Anvar.

'I'm adopted.'

Oh dear. Plan foiled. If a man hates his mum he's screwed up and dislikes all women because she never protected him or loved him. He therefore can't believe that women are worthy of emotional investment. I've watched Oprah you know.

'Adopted. Oh. Have you ever tried to contact your birth parents?' I ask, as gingerly as the sauce.

'No. I hate them. They gave me up.'

'I see.'

Yikes. Issues, in neon-red bulbs.

'So who brought you up then?' Down, down, Anvar the journo.

'I waz adopted by an elderly couple when I was seven. They were very kind Mormons and zey brought me up to respect the values of the Mormon teachings.'

'Sorry?'

'I'm adopted by Mormons.'

Yikes again!

'What, like The Osmonds?' C'mon, that's everybody's cultural reference.

'Zey, zos peoples, a rock band, huh! Zey are not the best example of our religion,' he's saying.

'Oh, I know,' I hear myself cackling, 'all that bad behaviour they specialised in, all the sex, drugs and rock 'n' roll they were famous for, no wonder you feel shame. You could not have suffered worse PR.'

I was prepared for Jeremy to be some kind of Christian, even one with a missionary's zeal, but I am not prepared to move to Utah.

'But you are a Muslim, Anvar?'

Come again?

'You are a Muslim. Mormons are very tolerant of all faiths. Zis is why I know we are getting on, because we respect each other and each other's God.'

Oh no.

'Jeremy, I don't have a God.'

'Anvar, you cannot disown Him.'

I live in Geeksville! You know, even Oprah, as I see it, well, she may be every woman's confidante, but if I told her about my life and times, even she would laugh at me hysterically, and say I have really bad luck with men.

'No, Jeremy, you don't get it – I do not believe in God. Okay, so sometimes I feel I am not alone, but that's usually post-vodka paranoia and now I accept that the aliens are not coming to get me, but I do not believe in any God.'

'Anvar,' Jeremy is whispering, 'zat is very bad – you can't say zese things.'

I don't get this. What is going on? Is it because I don't 'believe', that someone up there is taking the piss?

I can't even introduce this guy to my mates or even pretend he could be a boyfriend. What can be more impossible for close friends and colleagues to deal with than him choosing to be a Mormon?

I might as well shack up with a gay white trannie who wants to be a black transsexual. He reeks of freak, and I've had enough of those.

And me? Poor moi. The woman who bothered to go speed dating in the vain hope that she might meet a normal man.

What a start!

I am not destined to wait in the car while he goes chapping on innocent people's doors. I've never been a God-botherer and I ain't going out with one.

Bye bye Mormon from Morden.

Careful not to use the words God or Jesus, a few drinks at a whisky bar and I go off home realising I may never be struck by the lightening of love, just always dodging the thunderbolts.

6 February
3pm

Writing a column on women and handbags.

Goes like this: The reason women carry a bag and feel lost without one predates Furla and Prada.

When we were in bear skins and wearing bone jewellery our main job apart from giving birth was to collect berries and herbs and leaves while the men went out hunting for meat.

Problem was the men didn't actually secure a kill that often. Sometimes their skills with spears suffered from late nights clubbing, and so the tribe was mostly reliant on what the women brought back to the cave.

Men were the hunters, we were the gatherers. Yes, we had to

pat hubby on the head and reassure him that altho' he hadn't brought home any dinosaur or mammoth meat we didn't think any less of him as a man. Meanwhile, we went out scratching for so many healthy options we needed a large sack, for the roots, and another for the baby.

This means that women are primevally conditioned to carry a cloth they can bind, or the handbag as we now call it.

And as for the authoritative club that men used to carry in those days? Well, we all know they've swapped it for the modern-day equivalent of the remote control.

5.16pm

Landline call. No number comes up.

'Anvar, hi, it's me.'

You'll have to give me more to go on than that, matey. I sigh and wait for clarification.

'It's Frank, Professor Sullivan.'

'Oh. What do you want?'

'Anvar . . . oh Anvar . . .' He's wheedling me, he's actually coming on like we had a tiff.

'Anvar? I miss you Anvar.'

Nah. Bollocks.

'Anvar . . . can we start again?'

'Look, Frank, whatsyername, I don't want you calling me, because I don't want to speak to you, because, frankly, and that's not a pun, I don't fancy you, I don't want to see you again and I don't even like you! I spent a lot of money on our so-called affair and some recompense for that would be appreciated. Just send me a cheque.'

He's giggling away here.

Lose it. Big time.

'And by the way! Your shit smells mate. And you're full of it. Posing tosser. I hate veggies! It's not what you eat in the world it's what you do in the world that counts. Don't you know that?'

He comes off the blower like a chastened little boy. Should have tied him and whipped him when I had the chance.

'Oh okay, Anvar, bye then.'

Dork.

8pm

Getting dressed up to go out. Suede boots, thong soaked in eau de parfum, cleavage glitter and a black leather bondage cuff.

Sigh. Look out the window at N1 traffic, and take a deep breath in expectation of another night swinging from the chandeliers. Literally.

Sigh again.

Realise there's a single woman with four cats and a window box in all of us and indications show that the sooner I find her, the better.

9pm

Shane likes my outfit. Seems to think I'm wearing it for him.

'Wow. First date, great gear, let me look at you! Whoo-ooh! Smart laydee.'

He's slumming it in tropical beach wear even tho' we are in central London. He's mixed up. A bit like those who have four by fours but don't know where the countryside is.

'Yep, let's have slammers baybee. Hey Chico! Tequila love juice for us tonight! Hey Chico, tell Anvar what happened when we went surfing down under! Whoo-oh, the sharks man, and we weren't even in a cage looking at 'em. They were way up close man. I could see their fillings man.'

'Where were you then?' I ask.

'He was in Deep Sea World behind a glass,' says Chico.

'Huh! Yeah right man. Huh, yeah right man. Shut up man.'

Fear that Shane's diet consists of e numbers, E and also lots of Charlie.

11.22pm

Lock-in at Chico's place.

'See, thing is this . . .' I'm saying. 'You have to do it the Glaswegian way.'

'Yeah man yeah, Glasgow is happening man! Chico and me, we been to Glasgow.'

'It was Edinburgh,' says Chico.

'And we do it differently,' I'm swaying. 'Glaswegians do it different to Edinburghensians, we, the Celts, do it different to the Spanish and the English . . . it's a nationalistic thing . . .'

I solemnly approach.

'Watch me.' I'm hanging onto the stool, pouring salt onto the bar in a line, with the lemon and tequila on stand-by.

'In Glasgow,' I snarl, using my best James Cosmo impersonation, say, when he's playing a Scots psycho, 'we call it the Kamikaze Tequila.'

Chico and Shane and other assorted bums with bum fluff beards go silent. I mount the stool, and they begin to cheer and shout me on.

'Oi, oi, oi, oi, oi, oi, oi, oi, OI, OI, OI, OI, OI, OI'

I snort the salt, knock back the tequila and squeeze the lemon into my right eye.

'Hard as fuck, yahoo-oooooo!'

'Cool chick mate.'

'Thanks mate.'

'Fucking Glasgow, let's hear it for Glasgow!'

Shit, I've blinded myself.

12.30am

And we're singing . . . and staggering and scaring taxi drivers . . . who aren't stopping, because we're arm-in-arm, murdering a song by Terrorvision.

'. . . the curse of tequila tells you you're thirsty, tells you you're sober, then it's all over, over . . . that's the curse of tequila

. . . they'll tell you you're fine . . . con tequila, it feels fine, con tequila, when the doors are opened, and con tequila when they're calling time . . .'

3.20am
Lying on the floor. Dunno where. Really bad carpet. Scratchy too.

3.40am
Can't sleep. Find bedroom. Man in bed. Don't care. Crash out beside him.

6am
Wake up with a start! I'm upright. I'm dizzy. Pull blanket away from guy's face. That's not Shane.

6.30am
Can't close my eyes. Take another look.

6.45am
Fuck, it's Chico! Hey Chico! No, Anvar, don't talk to him. Lie down again.

8am
A hand swings over to sit on my thigh. Could be a sleepy mistake. Answers soon provided.

   Hand starts stroking my skin. Pushing my legs apart. Firmly. He still hasn't turned round. Fingers follow the line of my Brazilian. Feel like the legs of a spider. I'm wet. I'm such a whore but I know the score.

8.20am
I come hard. He takes his hand away and goes back to sleep. My temples feel tight. I get up. Look for my coat. Stand in the

doorway. Check him out. A head on the pillow. A hand he has now placed near his face, breathing it in. No movement. I leave.

8 February

12 noon

Ding dong. Text from Nigel, asking me to call him.

'Hey, Nigel, where are you?'

'Anvar, I'm just outside Heathrow, trying to get into inner London, traffic's murder.'

'You mean we can meet up? Great!'

'Am trying really hard babe. Aiming for say, being there at yours, say within two hours. You free? I mean, I don't want to presume you're free. I know I've been letting you down by not making it. It's just work hon, that's all.'

He sounds genuinely frustrated.

Bingo! Two hours!

12.15pm

In the bath. Shaving legs and armpits. Use an aromatherapy soap in chocolate, rose and ylang ylang and wonder if the bar was made by women who are pregnant and have odd cravings.

Applying Dior body lotion, baby oil on legs, scented deodorant under arms, perfume on pulse points with a little skoosh on my crotch; apply face pack, pluck eyebrows, trim pubes with nail scissors, blow dry hair, straighten hair with tongs, lashings of eight hour face cream and beauty flash balm, paint nails, paint toe-nails, put on stockings, suspenders, matching lingerie, a short black dress and a vintage diamante choker and all not necessarily performed in this order.

1.40pm

Ready!

2.30pm
No sign of him.

3pm
Wonder if I should phone him. I mean, he's on his way, right?
Busy man, just held up is all.

3.45pm
Text Nigel.

> U ok? Anvar x

4pm
Call him. Goes straight to voicemail. Bizarre.

5pm
Moby rings. Hesitate before answering. Slightly unnerved. Don't
know whether to have a hissy fit or play it cool. Go for Swedish
neutrality.
'Nigel, what's happened?'
'Anvar, it's a nightmare. Car's broken down.'
'What, the Lamborghini?'
I know nothing about cars yet figure that the fastest ones
aren't supposed to cop it when you have to follow a speed limit
of 30mph.
'No, I had to borrow one of my employee's cars, and drive it
to London for him, but, oh, can't believe it. Spent the last two
hours trying to pull it off the road, no one stopped to help, I mean
people are so selfish nowadays, Anvar, the world's gone mad.'
'Yes, it has.'
But what about me, me, ME!
'Look babe, doesn't look as if I'll be able to see you. There's
an engineer from my company on his way out to see me, and the
AA are coming . . . oh no . . .'

'What?'

The distant sound of sirens.

'Anvar, that's the police coming to check me out, wondering why I've been holding up the traffic trying to move this vehicle.'

'Look Nigel, I'll call you back.'

'No Anvar, my mobile batteries are low . . . hello? Still hear me? I need to use what's left to call my office. I'll try to call you tomorrow. Bye.'

6pm

Back from the off sales with three bottles of cava. Sit on bottom of bed and think. Don't get why Nigel hasn't made a single date. And when he calls from a car he always sounds as if he's phoning from under a cooker hood extractor.

8pm

Jacqui calls. Explain that I'm not feeling right about Nigel. Jacqui thinks he should be making more of an effort.

'I mean, Anvar what if you do go out with each other, that is, if you manage to meet up in the first place, and say you do get involved and it gets serious, what's he going to do, in that case, Mr Scarlet Pimpernel, Fedex the fucking ring?'

11pm

Lying on bed, listening to the city. Islington is quiet save the whooping that never stops; police, fire engines, unmarked panda cars. In London, you're never far from a siren.

14 February
8.45am

Run downstairs to see if there's any mail for me. Nope.

11am

Still waiting for flowers. A small bouquet even.

3pm

I mean, everyone knows I work from home, and I'm in all day to receive deliveries!

5.30pm

Live on the sofa with Channel 4's Richard and Judy, talking about Valentine's Day. Tell R&J that if I received any unsigned cards from anonymous men sent to my home address, I wouldn't think ooh, secret admirer, I'd think, oh no, stalker. I mean you just don't know who has access to the voting register nowadays.

11pm

St Valentine should be sued for further deflating already crumpled and spent ladies. Who was this fucker anyway, this man we all remember, whose name is in our calendars?

Some guy who is immortalised, a man who inspires other men to tell us girls how their hearts race and blood hastens when they see us. And then we are just so disappointed when we get nowt from the postie. Talk about being set-up. It's a conspiracy to keep us humble, being primed to want a man to want us. Gives us a wee boost you know, when a pink envelope flutters through the door. A shiver of adrenalin. Wow, St Valentine, whoever this man was, certainly keeps us on a drip.

Right. Look St Valentine up on the net. Yea, yeah, roses and lilies and chocolates, sweetmeats for sweethearts, get on with it. Aha! Huh? No way. The nerve!

The fucker was a man of God! Shocker! A monk no less! And what was a monk doing sending love letters to the laydeez anyway? Huh? These religious guys, they're all the same. A prostitute once told me that she is very busy during the Church of Scotland Assembly.

11.30pm
Ding Dong!
  AT LAST!
  A text. From Nigel. Says he's off to bed. 'Good night Anvar, sleep tight. Nigel.' That's quite nice of him.

15 February
7pm
Chico the serial masturbator is coming over. Don't expect to go out. Don't even expect to talk. It occurs to me that you can't find the word shame in my diary.

8pm
He's left. I offered him oral sex but he refused. He said what he was doing, turning me on, making me come, is what does it for him.
  I have never known a man who doesn't want a woman to go down on him.
  This, this is great; a guy who wants to give and does not take. A man, in fact, who doesn't want any sexual equality at all. Never a word said. I come, he goes. Perfect.
  Suspect he may be ashamed of the size of his penis. Being this generous just isn't normal.

20 February
1.30pm
Oh Chico! There's something unnerving about yelling 'Chico' during an orgasmic aria. Keep imagining myself in a headscarf after the cowboys have gone, having attacked my village, searching for my wounded Chico in the burning desert. Trying to drag him to a well for water, as he expires in the blistering sun, whispering in my ear, 'Tell Calamero, my son, I love him.

Oh Santa Maria.'

Then I scream his name, in much the same way as I do when I come.

MGM aren't in control of this script. Not that much of an Oscar-winning drama between us.

We're merely in a groove. Every second day, at noon I leave my front door ajar, lie on my bed, legs rudely apart, reading. Chico lets himself in, drinks a full glass of water in the kitchen, and walks through to my bedroom where I ignore him.

He strokes my tiny pouch, my Lilliputian hammock of a gusset, until it is sodden, then he takes my book from me, and lifts me until I am on his knees. He puts an arm around me, smiles into my eyes, and weaves his fingers into my pants, a finger on my pearl, that swells and hardens as I jerk into his hand.

Funny thing is, I'm not even sure I fancy him.

21 February
6.15pm
Moby's going off. I'm hungover. Ugh, sweaty palms. I've got the shakes, the fucking shakes!

'Hi Anvar, it's Kelvin.'

Bugger calls me from a private number. A successful dupe. Respect.

'Where are you gorgeous?'

'In the flat working the laptop.' *Well, I'm just about to. Logging in.*

'You'll never guess what I woke up this morning thinking?'

'What, Kelvin?' I'm asking.

Doesn't he ever go away?

'I was thinking about you, and you'll never guess what I had?'

'Tell me then.'

Shit. Can't recall my password.

'A hard-on. It was bulging. And who do you think it was for?'

Funny, have a sense I should be doing something today.

'My hard-on. It was all for Anvar.'

'Huh?'

I'm checking my emails.

'Yes, and I've got one now, and who is it for?'

'Er . . .'

Arse. Three emails marked high priority. What's Kelvin muttering about? A present for me? More underwear, yes!

'Yes, Kelvin, the package is for me.'

'Yes, all for Anvar, and what would you like me to do with it?'

'Huh?'

Shit, an email from the BBC. Loads of research to do before I present on the World Service. Tomorrow!

'Will it be a) lying back on the bed while you talk dirty? b) letting me slowly wank off Excalibur, all for you? or c) telling me how you'd like to fuck me? And that you want to be on top, because you're a very dominating woman.'

'Er . . .'

Can't believe I forgot I'm on air tomorrow.

'Er . . . b, then.'

'Oh you sexy girl. I read your column on threesomes last week, and you'll never guess what effect it had on me?'

'No . . .'

I'm usually so on my broadcasting game.

'I got a hard-on, it was monstrous.'

'Oh I see.'

Now where's my script?

'Would you have a threesome with me?'

'Sure, yes, sure, I agree, that sounds right. Whatever you say Kelvin.'

I am usually never this unprofessional.

'Oh you sexy girl. Would you like me to come for you now?'

'Er . . . sure . . . yeah. Yup. Yep. Send it right over to me.'

'Oh you sexy girl.'

A woman just doesn't know what she's doing unless she follows the script and remembers to speak right on cue.

'And who am I coming for?'

'Er . . .'

Lost the plot. Coming for? What's he on about?

'Yes, yes, it's all for Anvar . . . ugh . . .'

This is not a great line to Scotland. There's probably a storm.

'I want you to be in . . . control . . . uh . . . uh . . . ugh . . . uhuhuhuhuhuhuh . . . oh . . . oh . . .OH!'

Aha! Script is in the wordworks file. At last. Thought I was a goner. Really have to call time with the phone.

'Bye Kelvin, thanks for calling, and for the underwear you're sending me.'

7 March

3pm

Back from an audition for ITV's *Loose Women*. Didn't get it. The irony is not lost on me.

4pm

Oh, look at the time, Nigel says he's going to phone around now. Been thinking about him.

He's been in Ireland for a couple of weeks. Called me on a couple of occasions, said he was with some cousins and living it large. Yet still . . . he always has the same backdrop of noise; either a noisy hum of an engine or complete quiet, in a place that slightly echoes, like a toilet.

Och, I'm imagining things. The man's kosher. Has to be. Speed daters are vetted, aren't they? So they are who they say they are. Maybe not, actually.

Still, something up with this. Just a feeling I have that . . . oh, here he is on the blower as usual.

'Hi Nigel.'

'Anvar, babe, how's you?'

'Cool.'

I'm going to put my foot down, like I wish Nigel has many times, but there's not enough of the Mansell in him.

'Nigel, when are we going to meet again? This has been going on for ages.'

'Oh Anvar, I know, I'm sorry. Every time I say to myself, right, I'm going in to central London to see Anvar, something happens. I get, uh, so frustrated. I'm dying to see you. I just think someone up there doesn't like me.'

I can sympathise with him there.

'Nigel, can I have your email?'

'What? You're breaking up Anvar.'

'CAN I HAVE YOUR PERSONAL EMAIL? I tried the business one you used before but it keeps bouncing back.'

Silence.

'I want to send you an invite to a media party, you'd like it, there'll be loads of interesting people there, film directors and editors and producers . . .'

'Anvar sorry, I'm going to have to hang up, I'm not on speakerphone, I'm using a handset and that's illegal. I can see a police car. In my position Anvar, I don't need any . . . burrrrr . . .'

'But Nigel I . . .'

Shit.

10 March
10.30am

Ding Dong! No mobile, no life. Text from Mikey!

Anvar, I hope there's nothing wrong. U haven't called me 4 mths. I hope u r ok. London can b tuff and I want u to no I care. I am here 4 u and always will b. Call me. Mike.

Fuck off.

11.45am

Chico's in touch. He's in the area, well, he always is really.

Text: Anvar, fancy a wank in 10 mins?
Me: Yes!

Ooops, actually, diary's a bit full today, gotta make calls.

Me again: Can we make it 1230 tomorrow?

It's really important to be spontaneous.

1pm

Making plans for Nigel. I really like him. Or p'raps I like the idea of a safety net, of never having to work again, of never worrying that I might end up penniless and withered and suffering severe water retention around the ankles.

But I am attracted by the idea of a man who gets what he wants, as Nigel seems to.

You know. He might be being cagey because he's used to being hounded by gold diggers! That's it! A guy in his position, like he says, he could be stung really badly by some material girl, some sociopath.

It's genuine tho', at least, the interest a woman feels in a man who is rich enough to have any woman he wants.

Do like the fact he's a man in control, a success, a king of the jungle. And this from the girl who swore at 14 that she'd earn every penny she spent herself. Now I'm thirtysomething, I'm talking like a hooker.

I'll have you know, that it takes a lot of mental and emotional discipline, staying on the straight and shallow.

11 March
2pm

In Chinatown at Mr Kong's restaurant to meet Heidi's new bloke. She's like me; her bedroom door is a revolving one. Interrupt a conversation about vibrators.

'Vibrators are a godsend but they're too noisy,' Heidi's saying.

'Do you masturbate?' Teddy's asking me.

Realise I'm expected to join in a frank, open discussion in an open-plan bar where Heidi and Teddy can parade their 'we can talk about anything, can't we toots?' relationship.

Not up for it.

Bitter and twisted today, like my favourite cocktails.

'Yes, I do masturbate Teddy,' I hear myself saying. 'Especially now I've given up smoking. I need something to do with my hands. But I'm trying not to masturbate in all the places I used to smoke, like bars and at dinner and outside the fire exit, or in the smoking room at the office. A lot of people are very intolerant about wanking yourself off in public nowadays. You can suffer from passive orgasm. In fact, when I see signs saying "No Masturbating" I just take myself outside to have one.'

10.33pm

'You've lost it Anvar,' says Heidi on the phone.

'No, I haven't, I'm just . . . disillusioned.'

'Teddy was only trying to make conversation.'

Was he fuck, the jerk off little chancer. I'm getting angry with men. Really don't know what they're for.

12 March
7pm

'Don't you just work from your office?' I'm asking Nigel, concerned he may be slumming it, a man in his position too.

'Well, everyone says that to me, but I like to be hands-on.'

He's in one of his cars, of course. 'I'm not the kind of boss who doesn't want to know his employees. I want to be at every meeting, simple as that. Clocked up 30,000 miles on this baby already this year.'

Shouldn't be suspicious of the man, he's a sound guy who cares about his workers.

'So what is your email Nigel?'

'Ah, Anvar, meant to talk to you about that. I don't have an email,' he's shouting.

That's impossible.

'But I'm always available on fax. I'll get my secretary to call you with the number.'

9.45pm

Okay, he takes a while to respond to texts. And his moby is always on voicemail when I dial him spontaneously. But, you know, this is the 21st century. And everyone has an email address. I'm running it all past Jacqui again who is snorting with derision.

'Anvar, that doesn't sound right to me,' she's saying.

'Well, it's queer, I admit.'

'You can't have a relationship with a man who's always available on fax.'

'This isn't making sense,' I puzzle.

'No one faxes anymore, full stop. A guy who is what he says he is should have an email. Get real. Could you imagine telling anyone in your entire business career or any of your friends that you are always available on fax? Seriously?'

10.15pm

What is going on here? Do you really need the cynicism of Poirot and the observance of Sherlock Holmes nowadays to go out with a guy?

A rich guy could possibly be eccentric. But with all his travelling and his host of cars and his rally driving and his planes, Nigel just can't handle any degree of geography to fulfil a mere date.

I Shagged A Serial Killer

14 March
2.30pm
On a train to Windsor. Nigel called this morning and says he's stuck in a house there looking after one of his employee's dogs as a favour he can't get out of. Says the dog's only three and a handful. Sitting here mulling over why people bother to have pets, especially when you can get fertility treatment on the NHS.

4pm
I'm here. No sign of Nigel. Linger on the platform, admiring the potted plants. Hate suburbia. Think it's where people go to hide.

4.10pm
On the street outside the entrance. In a top hat and sunglasses. Smoking. Got here like a stranger on a train. You can tell I'm an outsider.

4.15pm
On the phone Nigel suggested we go for a drink, then, he says, we'll have to go back to the house for the dog. It doesn't like being without human company apparently. Oh, the need to be needed really makes a nurse out of all of us.

4.16pm
Call him. He asks me what I can see. I say the great view of a Harvester pub and a car park. Says he'll be with me in a twinkle. Feel really spaced.

4.20pm

Aha! I see a Jaguar pulling up across the road. It's stopped! Yeah! Must be him. Wave. Wave again. Driver's just sitting there. Think of walking over. Something stops me. The guy gets out, and locks up. It's not Nigel.

4.21pm

With the shocker of Nigel being late and getting excited about the wrong car, I feel like I'm being mocked.

4.25pm

Nigel arrives on foot, out of nowhere. He isn't as attractive as I remember him. He is shorter, looking chubby from a diet of heart attack material and beer, rather than salmon and bubbly. Doesn't seem that relaxed. He has the air of the driven, in the sense that he seems very much in the present but you know more important matters are preying on his mind.

4.26pm

He kisses me lightly on the cheek and loops his thumb into his belt as we walk to a local bar. We make polite chit chat. 'I'm selling my Aston Martin,' he announces.

'Oh?'

'Yep, the James Bond one. Forty-two grand. I bought it for sixty, off a Hollywood director, but, well, I don't mind the loss. Know anyone who'd want to buy it?' Have a sense of déja vu, as if he's talked to me about James Bond before.

'I really don't know anyone with that kind of money, Nigel,' I'm answering with a gasp.

He's going red.

'Nigel, why do you always talk about money?' I'm mincing along at quite a fast pace here, trying to keep up with him. Catch my reflection in a shop window. In the hat, I look like one of those witches you see in horror movies who elevate skilfully across the room a few inches above the floor.

'Sorry Anvar, I'm so ashamed. I wasn't brought up to talk about money, my mother always warned me about that, it's not like me, not at all, that's really bad, I must work on that, sorry.'

Gosh, he seems so upset. Kick myself. Shouldn't have said anything.

4.35pm

In some dark, wooden theme bar with the remains of a rum do on all around. I choose a table beside a tagliatelle of paper chains, some shredded poppers lying like frayed tassels on the floor, and a wilted candle, a deformed shape that Doris Stokes would be proud of summoning, and which is stuck on a rippled beer mat. The party's over for somebody.

Nigel is massaging his jeans pocket before pulling out some smash. I guess he suffers from a sort of Bill Gates modesty.

I order a bottle of Becks because it's buy one get one, and that means he gets a free drink.

I fully intend that he decipher my eye for a bargain as me not being and never having been a woman who throws money around or indeed would ever expect a man to order champagne just because he is a multi-millionaire. If he mentions Bond Street I'll pretend to never have heard of it.

Here we are, drinking beer on special offer, in the kind of casual poverty only the wealthy can enjoy.

5.35pm

Feel really odd. Nigel keeps talking about how the ex-mistress of a high profile politician, and a close friend, keeps nagging him about funding a pilot TV series. I tell Nigel, channels commission what they want to broadcast and give companies the money to make programmes. Strange, weird and discomfiting that a man who is worldly-wise and who has contacts in Hollywood thinks a private investor will get a programme on the TV.

6pm

Tediously, back to Nigel's employee's house for the dog.

My instinct is saying something is not right. Decking my conscience, sitting on its chest so it can't speak and I can't hear it anymore.

I mean, I'd rather get laid, I've been waiting for this for a while.

6.10pm

Standing on the pavement trying to cross a road to get to the house. Nigel's head is acting like he's in the audience at Wimbledon. Realise we've been waiting on the kerb for a while.

There's a dozen cars, all going at less than 30mph, and Nigel is grabbing my arm.

I'm all for wading through them, skipping past the bonnets, nipping in and out of the bumpers. I live in London after all. If you always waited on the green man to light up, in total you would lose as many years of life as you do when you are sleeping.

'No, be careful,' Nigel's remonstrating. 'We'll wait here.'

'Fuck's sake. We can get across.'

'No, it's safer to wait,' insists Nigel.

'But they're not even going fast.' I laugh. 'Come on!'

I see some sweat on Nigel's top lip. He is quiet, he seems distant, and in no way prepared to risk being run over, even when there is as little chance of that as in a car showroom.

I humour him, think this panic of his is cute.

And then the thought that I shoo away, like an annoying fly, how he can speed at motor rallies, fly planes that flip over, or risk piloting a helicopter in strong winds when he is scared of the traffic in a small, parochial street.

Anvar, it doesn't fit. Anvar, go back to London!

6.20pm

Turning solidly and determinedly into a little sanctuary of semi-detached, Victorian sandstone houses, all very quiet and twee. Suburbia, at its net-curtained, dysfunctional and secretive best.

6.21pm

Nigel is opening the front door. I'm checking the motors parked in the street for a possible vehicular suspect in the strange case of Nigel's invisible collection of expensive cars.

And then it happens.

'Shit. Jesus Christ! No! No! No! Help! Get off me! No! I'm scared. Please Nigel. No! Help me. Please get him off me. Someone please. Oh Lord.'

I'm scared. I'm falling onto the ground. I'm being dragged into the house. The door is closing behind me.

'It's okay,' Nigel is laughing. 'He's harmless.'

6.22pm

I see pellets of foamy saliva on my coat. I smell of biscuity mucus. Scooby Doo, with the same level of brains but without the charm, is pawing me, its mouth dripping globular, excretory, milky strands over my chest as I sit on the couch in the living room.

Nigel is showing me how tall the Great Dane is.

'Look, Anvar, he's on his hind legs! Six foot tall! Amazing, eh?'

Yes, wonderful, especially when 'it' launches itself at you and you experience the full force of a Shetland pony on heat.

'He sits on the couch you know,' Nigel is saying, 'just like a person.'

The dog leans back and parks its quarters and its jumbo sausage roll of an ass onto the sofa, its front paws on the floor. 'It' is taking up the whole three-seater, squishing me into indignity.

Notice Nigel is chuckling and is gazing at the Great Dane adoringly. He is ignoring me and whooping with delight and cuddling and wrestling with this canine catastrophe.

Think the dog obviously loves him. Shit. In fact. In fact . . .
the dog KNOWS him.

Wait a minute, Anvar, do you know what you are saying?
Listen to yourself woman.

I mean, 'it' didn't jump HIM at the door did it? Didn't even
bark at Nigel. Even if he dog-sat, say, once a month, another
man's dog would surely whine a little, if not at least yelp and
growl at a strange male in his owner's house?

'Do you fancy a drink?' Nigel is asking, locking the horse out
into the hallway.

'Erm . . .'

This isn't making sense. A guy as busy as Nigel wouldn't be
dog-sitting on a regular basis anyway.

'Beer?' Nigel's in the kitchen doorway. I jump.

'Sure.'

6.23pm

Silence. The Great Dane is sniffing under the door, vacuuming
up our smells with its cow nostrils.

Ugh, this is an ugly room. Cramped, busy, with flowery
wallpaper and acrylic curtains.

Funny.

Nigel is walking straight to the kitchen fridge, and pulling
out a bottle opener from a drawer; he doesn't even have to hunt
for it.

6.25pm

I can't look at him. Find myself staring at a large globe standing
in the corner behind a chair and an apology of a rubber plant.

'George Harrison gave me that.'

'Sorry?'

'You've heard of the The Beatles? Yeah? George Harrison, I
bought it off him, at a charity auction. I always said to him I

liked it. I gave it to my mate as a gift for all his hard work.'

The cold beer tips into my mouth, and floods the pouch of my lower lip. I have upturned the bottle, have fed myself the malty, fizzy liquid, but I can't remember doing it.

In my mind, I'm tracing my fingers over the globe, I'm looking for marks in cities and countries where he has a relationship with unsuspecting women, who think his work takes him all over the world.

Stop it Anvar! The dog spooked you is all. This kinda shit doesn't happen. Pull yourself together. But 'George Harrison'? I mean, I've questioned Nigel's authenticity before, and now, yet, that one name, that one remark, it seems like one lie too many . . .

'What do you think of the décor? Hmm? Not up to much is it. I don't think they've got much taste.'

'They?'

'Yes, him, my associate and his wife. What kind of interior design do you like?' He is standing by the fireplace, and is crossing one leg over the other, his elbow balancing on the mantelpiece. Mr Cool.

'I like minimalism,' I'm countering. I don't, I'm fibbing. I'm egging him on, just to see, just to test him. 'Buddhisty, stark sort of Anoushka Hempel styles.'

'Oh, I know her,' Nigel's saying, mid-swig.

NO YOU FUCKING DON'T!

'Do you want a tour?' Oh mate, that's the most crap excuse to get me to the bedroom I've ever heard.

'Yes, I need to go to the loo, if you don't mind.'

'Sure.'

6.40pm

He's climbing the stairs and I'm following him. I turn to see if the front door has been locked. Shit, he's glancing round, he just saw me do that, lunge in towards the keyhole. Waiting for a sarky comment. Nope. He doesn't seem perturbed, doesn't comment on it, he keeps climbing and I keep following.

'This is the main bedroom,' he's saying, pushing his leaking, heavy breathing, manic, pedigree chum into a storage outlet.

I'm poking my head in. Don't care about the damn 'tour'.

Oh yes, nice.

I see a crowded space with a four-poster, decked out in old and faded Laura Ashley fabrics.

Thing is, the room seems empty. I'm looking at it, surveying it, thinking that with all that colourful, ethnic tat – bedspreads, cushions, pillows, antimacassars, in the kind of pronounced Egyptian print you'd have to put a rainbow through a Kaleidoscope to get – the room, it's bizarre, because the room, it looks cosy yet bare. I mean, you'd think someone who liked such busy bedspreads and rugs would have stacks of stuff; photographs, books, glass ornaments, perfumes, pastel coloured tissues, antique vases, car boot sale oil paintings. It looks like a raggedy and feminine room waiting for a woman to move in.

I shrug.

Must move on.

'The bathroom is there. Take your time,' he's smiling.

'Thanks. With you in a minute.'

The second bedroom looks like a spare, with cardboard boxes in the corner bulking up the small space, with a throw over the top of them to hide the contents.

'I'll be in here, attending to a couple of things, take your time.'

6.43pm

No toilet roll. I don't believe it. Toilet roll, schmoilet roll . . . I'm looking around me on the floor, a sort of grey concrete. Has there been a fucking burglary?

Nope, no spare rolls to be seen. Cotton wool! Yes, Nigel's employee's wife/partner/whatever, she's bound to have some of that somewhere.

Nah, don't see any toiletries yet.

Oh, a small hand towel. No Anvar, that's a minging thing to do.

Pissing like a donkey here, all that beer. Think I'll sit here for a mo' and gather my thoughts, they're like a coup of unruly chickens that have escaped and are squawking and clucking all over the yard.

That fucking hound is sniffing under the door. Dirty, clodhopping meathead!

Am I on a farm?

'You alright?' Nigel is calling for me from the spare bedroom. 'Fine, thanks!'

We're going to fuck, I know we're going to fuck. Maybe that's why I'm nervous, it's been gaining momentum for a couple of months, this liaison, we've been giggling and speaking and texting and now, we're in the same house, in the same city, and finally my glory hole will be having her debut.

Still, this is a weird home.

No wastepaper basket. Shit. No soaps, or bubble bath, don't see any deodorants, or body sprays, or lotions . . . wait a minute. Right, will just have to squat here and drip for a bit . . . don't see any paraphernalia at all. Oh, there's a mirrored cupboard above the sink. Just shake it, Anvar, pull up the g-string, there. Hate doing that.

Now, I'm up. Open the cabinet. Nothing. NOTHING! I'm swinging round. Nothing personal at all. No hair gels, combs, clips, razors, tweezers, shampoos, toothpastes, toothbrushes.

I feel in a bit of a tizzy.

Better, er, better get out of the toilet.

6.50pm

Nigel's in the spare room, smiling and looking out of the window. It's sunny.

'Where's the er . . .'

'Oh, I put him in the bedroom,' says Nigel. The beast is digging at the threshold with its leonine paws. The dumb fuck really thinks that will work.

Joining Nigel I peer out and see an adjoining garden where a man is inspecting his flower beds, and mulling about his lawn.

'Not a nice man, that,' says Nigel.

'Oh? How do you know that?'

'Oh, my mate built an extension downstairs and he complained to the council.'

Is this small talk?

Anvar, keep the window open, that man down there is the only person around who might hear you scream.

'Yes, he objected to the council about the extension my friend built. Horrible busybody.'

Even better, Anvar! This nosey neighbourhood jobsworth would definitely report anything untoward.

Oh God, Nigel is leaning in, he's kissing my neck. Uh! He's biting my neck! Uh, this feels good. Shit I'm really turned on.

6.51pm

Nigel is guiding me over to a single bed. The one beside all the cardboard boxes.

He's stroking my hair. Shit, he's biting an artery. Damn, I'm on fucking fire! What is going on?

I was scared a minute ago, terrified.

Oh oh. He's turning me away from him, sliding my jeans over my hips. He is strong! Ah! His nails are digging into the flesh at the top of my butt.

Ow! I'm stepping out my trousers like I'm settling into a pair of skis.

I am so wet. Can't believe this. Never felt so much adrenalin since doing a parachute jump . . . I'm holding my breath. I can't exhale. Aw! His thumbs are pulling the straps of my thong away from my body and down, down . . . I am so lush with this . . .

oh, my g-string is hesitating, sticking to my cunt . . . he's pulling them off me, down to my knees.

And we're on the bed.

I'm on fire, I'm on fire . . . want to fuck like cavewoman. He's staring at me, he looks amused, why is he doing that? Oh, shit, oh, oh, oh, yes, oh no, oh no, yes, yes, harder, harder, oh shit I'm coming, harder, shit, yes, yes, yes, shit I'm coming . . . no don't come inside me Nigel, don't come inside me, shit, stop. What do you mean 'no'. Oh, oh, stop. Put it on. Put the condom on Nigel, DON'T FUCK WITH ME I'M A WOMAN WHO'S ABOUT TO COME!!! Inside me, again, please, shit, oh yes, NIGEL, AAAA-EEEE-UUUUUHHHH-OOOOO-OH OH Oh Oh Oh oh ohhhh . . . wow. Oh wow.

Happy to keep moving so that he can . . . have some pleasure . . . funny . . . just thinking . . . about where I am. Oh my God, the thought is coming at me like a twister. It's his. The dog is his. This is his house, I'm in his home. The boxes, covered up, that's where he's put all his wife's stuff; her personal things, her toiletries, her make-up, that's why he was late in meeting me, he was tidying up, that's why there's nothing intimate in the bedroom, he's cleared it all away so I won't suspect anything . . . I'M IN HIS FUCKING HOME!

He's about to come. Get off me Nigel. Get off me, I mean it. I want out of here. I really want to go.

Too late.

He comes. I am in shock. Swing my legs over the side of the bed. Nigel wants a cuddle. No. No.

I dress. He dresses. Quickly. Nigel looks at his watch, murmurs something about the real dog-sitter arriving in forty minutes and he just has time to walk me to the station and have a drink on the way. Know he's lying, know there is no dog-sitter, know he has a partner. Know he's a fake.

Can't stop looking at his socks. They are personality socks, with motifs of Tweetie-Pie on them.

Walk out the front door to feel the sun on my face. We are walking in silence. Don't memorise the street names because I know I'm safe. I know I won't be back.

Keep thinking, thinking, that he doesn't want to kill me, not in that sense.

'Do you know,' Nigel is suddenly saying, 'I think I'll take a rain check on the drink. But what if I drive down tonight to London to see you? We could have dinner.'

'Yes,' I'm smiling. 'That'd be nice.'

'Anvar,' he says, as I break away and walk towards the station. 'You know I'm bad. And you're bad, just like me.'

7.30pm

On train. I'm staring out the window. A small area on my back feels nippy and painful.

9.30pm

Home. Check the scratch on the top of my left buttock where Nigel pulled down my jeans. It had been annoying me on my journey, itchy with sweat. It's deep. It's going to scar.

Be A Man In Bed
And The Bitch Will Follow

16 March
7pm

Ramone is on the moby.

He's in Agony Pants mode. He believes, like all gay men believe, that straight women know nothing about men.

'My gay friends,' he's saying.

'Ramone,' I'm countering before he goes off on one. 'I'm not gay. I am straight.'

'Yes, Anvar Dah-ling, one knows that, but you sleep with men don't you?'

'S'pose.'

'And so do I!'

One nil. Okay, now I'm listening.

'I've realised we all have really intense relationships with our one night stands. When you think about it Anvar, you have a really intimate encounter; attraction, passion and raucous, honest sex.'

'S'pose. I mean you want to do your best.'

'And I just think it's really difficult to let that excitement go. I mean, a one-night stand has the potential to become something else. You are so raw and so naked together.'

'Yeah but a one-night stand is just that,' I hear myself saying. 'It's like being under a spell; you look at him later and go ugh, and step back in amazement, and go, I just let that man inside me?'

'Anvar, I'm worried about you. You think you're in control but you're not. You bond with strangers, and then never want to see them again. Anvar, you think sex means nothing. But you want it to mean something. Really, you do. You want love. I think you have deep-seated intimacy issues and they have to be addressed before you run out of men to have sex with.'

This is difficult. Didn't know my life was upsetting people who care.

'Ramone, I ain't screwing around because I have low self-worth, I have never slept with a guy just so he'd like me more. I like sex okay! That's it. Do you have any idea how many women envy me being able to fuck and dump like I do? Ramone, go on, go away and have some sport sex, get shagged, take your mind off all this bull. I'm just finding this really tedious. Women can do casual sex.'

'No, Anvar,' Ramone's saying, close to tears. 'Women can't. You're a man, and it hurts me to know you're much more of a man than I am.'

8pm

Ding Dong. Text from Sam. Says Seamus and his wife have split. No happy endings are there, for anyone? Even for him who deserves one.

Wonder if Seamus will call me? No. He had his chance. I mean, he married someone else when he could have had me.

So glad I'm out of Glasgow. I'm happy here in London. Finally got to the stage where the men of my past are staying there.

Fridge Magnet Philosophy:
If that real and terrifying romantic love they talk about exists, it's <u>even more</u> frightening to know you can live without it because you have.

17 March
St Patrick's Day, 10.30am

Sitting here at my desk, with the window open, not enough oxygen in the humid sauna air to breathe. A fly with the body of a fat raisin is banging itself against the inside of the pane. Centuries of glass and the fuckers still haven't evolved to know how to get out of the room they flew into.

Feel like a corpse. Just lost my spirit completely.

What have I become? A woman, perhaps, who stubbornly refuses to give up her sexual freedom even when it seems to incarcerate her in transient pleasures granted by fleeting men.

Have to think about Nigel. Have to work this out.

I keep learning that men come in various shapes, colours and sizes, and with varying degrees of a personality disorder.

I can't deny my own experience. You have to keep your eyes wide open and at least some communication between your head and your heart.

We are surrounded by duplicitous men, and it is only when the dirty deed is done, when we start to fall in love, when the phone ringing is enough to induce sweat, palpitations and a delicious feeling of lust, that we are lost to such men.

What's that noise? A nasty, mournful zizzing sound. It's the fly. Oh, yuck, it's being embraced by a spider, which is wrapping its long, elegant pins around that furious fat black body, and twisting the fly turning it over and over, knitting it into a web, into a bobbin of spider's thread. So that's the noise a fly makes when it's being murdered, when the life is being squeezed out of it.

3pm

The darkness isn't going. Drink will make it worse.

Don't know what men like Nigel get out of conning women.

I need either a massage or a psychiatrist, dunno which one will make me feel better.

When you construct a future around a man, imagine being with him forever, or falling in love, thieves like Nigel should be up for assault and battery. They steal your hope and fray what little expectations you already possess about the opposite sex. If I wasn't cynical before now I am positively inured to men.

My heart is in a fucking cage.

I'm mad at myself, and I'm sad that I know so much about men I have no alternative but to hoover up my misty dreams of Mr Right, into some fat airbag, the very one that I fear I may become.

Nigel. You are a fantasist. It was never about sex for you was it? The kick is getting strong women to like, love and trust you. You get off on mixing with people of every class who think you are who you say you are.

You must have moaned with pleasure when you met me, a journalist you could dope up with falsehoods.

Nigel's arrogance is perfect, psychopaths are always full of conceit. Other human beings are set pieces in their little game of chess.

6pm

It's laughable. If it hadn't been for that stupid dog I wouldn't have a clue about his double life. They say dogs are the best detectives, they know the truth, you just have to watch them.

I just feel really sick with myself. I was in a situation I knew was dangerous and I stayed there and had sex with the man who was weaving me into his life of lies.

He is the ultimate misogynist, and he's still out there.

Retrospect is a great thing they say, and a sorry insight because you always need its wisdom now, in the present.

It's easy now to see the signs: he always called me, he made sure I never saw his car, the mysterious fax number, his naivety about the film industry – which figures because having looked at him on the net again, there is no factual information on him, only a suggestion that he was involved in a certain movie. It was my ambition and enthusiasm that put him at the centre of Hollywood success.

Thinking now that he may not even be using his real name.

Make coffee. Light a fag. Glance up at the dead fly. That spider jabbed its prey to death, as slowly and as sensitively as fingers in a velvet glove stretch out lazily to caress a precious stone.

7pm

It's the sex I'm worried about. Realise that this is the first time in my entire romantic career that I am disgusted with myself for enjoying it.

I knew I was fucking with a situation in which I was very vulnerable. Am feeling hopelessly twisted about this. Don't get why he turned me on.

Perhaps fear is the greatest aphrodisiac of all. Perhaps when a man and a woman know they are about to experience something horrific and pant-shittingly bad, you want the last act of life. You want sex. Who knows? Perhaps when the *Titanic* was sinking, people were fucking frantically. Who knows that if a plane was crashing down and you believed you were about to die, you wouldn't want a man inside you. Some healing. Sex is a form of primal desperation. It is not always about seeking pleasure. It's politics. A pacifier. An appeasement. A reassurance. Maybe like a female Bonobo I was subconsciously trying to calm him down and lessen the threat.

That's funny. I just made myself laugh. But it's not amusing really, because maybe that's what I did. In fright, you can take flight, fight or fuck, but only because you want to stay alive.

8pm

Drinking. Heavily. Go Out.

Wonder if Seamus is living the day up. He's Irish after all.

Me And The Female Porn Star
Get It On In Several Toilets

10.45pm

In a club in East London. TV party. Free bar. Oh so dangerous.

The younger guys don't look as if they ironed their own shirts. The knackered older ones don't even look as if they could carry the weight of their own erection.

Yep. It's not a great night for the guys. Hang out with cool chicks in corner.

'We saw you dancing to Abba and we knew you were one of us,' they are chirruping.

Female solidarity. We are all so fabulous in our transvestite glamour. Me in my black velvet top slashed to my belly, them in their bodices, kinky boots, brunette wigs, bling bling, high-octane make-up and buffed skin.

Rachel tells me she's a film star. Wow, I say, that's cool, really different and I ask her what she acts in and she says 'lesbian porn', and I go oh, cool, and look around me at the women I'm hanging out with and realise they are all in the sex industry.

Always fancied it myself. At least they have the nous to get paid for what I do for free.

Rachel keeps rubbing up against me.

She's not putting a show on for the men either.

And she's on the ball.

More lethal cocktails of Peach Snapps, Advocaat and Mint! Okay! Yes, I can drink mine quickly.

Oh, Rachel I feel like puking. No, I really do, drank them too fast, all four of them. Oh, dying.

Yeah, sure, you can come to the loo with me.

Ooops, sorry mate. Didn't see you there.

Look, Rachel, putting me over the seat like this is making me queasy. Nah, don't think I am going to be sick. No, you don't have to stroke my hair back from my face.

Yeah, it feels nice, sure it does. Right, let me get up!

Tee hee hee hee hee hee, uhuhuhuhuhuhuh . . . ooooooh dear. We are so ARSED!

No, you don't have to help me walk. Ooops. Slid on some water. You could get health and safety onto that. Oh no you can't. I spilt it.

Just wanna get to the sink.

Need to lean over it. Splash water onto face, neck and wrists. Oh that's good. Oh I am so HOT! Think I'm having an early menopause.

Rachel. Rachel? Rachel, where are you?

11.05pm

Turn round. Rachel is standing in front of me, close. I can feel her belt buckle on my pierced belly button.

She kisses me.

Jesus! She kissed me!

It's like I just noticed her. Australian. Blonde. Pretty. Looks like Cameron Diaz.

I am so DRUNK! Maybe she is Cameron Diaz.

Uh. Shit.

'I am such a dyke,' she says.

What is she doing?

Huh. This is funny.

A cold hand is under my top and touching my breast.

I'm smiling at her. I'm enjoying this. I really am.

Am amazed at how hard my nipples are.

She's pulling out my breast, holding it, stroking my nipple with her thumb and staring into my eyes, smiling in a goofy, girlie way.

'So what do you do? Really?' I'm asking, bearing in mind I've been adopted by a band of Amazonian gals who drink from the fairy cup.

'I'm a porn star,' she says. 'Anya directs me. You met her, huh?' Rachel's stroking my neck. I can see it now. We're on candida camera.

'She's my girlfriend.'

Aaarrrgghh! Oh no, Boudicca meets Zena Warrior Princess, they're going to assemble, scream, raise their spears and cut my hair off. Then throw me to the men.

'Won't Anya be upset at you, er, seducing me?'

'We have an arrangement.'

11.30pm

On my knees in cubicle number eight; they hurt. They must really be raw for me to feel them. After all, when I go out, someone alerts the breweries. Jaw's sore too. This is hard work.

'Uh, uh, uh, oh, oh OH OH OH!'

I'm a girl and I know what does it for me, and I can't believe that Rachel is this turned on. Makes me think even dykes fake it, but surely the female orgasm isn't so complicated that even your own kind can't get you there?

'Fist me now, fist me, fist me.'

How the hell do I do that? The woman's a porn star for God's sake. I have performance anxiety.

'Now fuck me, fuck me, fuck me . . .'

Eh? How does that work? What is she on about?

Rachel is sitting on the toilet tank, legs wide open, shrieking like a banshee. I can hear other toilets flushing and people rolling down the towel to dry their hands. Think she thinks she's doing the audio for one of her movies.

'Lick me, lick me, lick me.'

This is like working on a coalface. Also for some reason feel my life lately has been dogged by toilet bowls but can't recall why.

18 March
12.30am

In Balans, Soho. Rachel, me and Anya. I keep passing out. Hear snatches of chat out of context as if I'm running through a noisy crowd.

'I love the way you lick me,' is whispered into my ear, Anya has her hand down the seat of my jeans. I'm a victim. I'm being raped by the Sapphic Women. 'Let's go to the toilet,' she says. God, women are demanding.

Actually think that if I lock myself into a cubicle I'll be able to get a sleep.

Try to close the door, Anya elbows her way in after me, and pushes me onto the floor. Sits on the toilet tank. I'm knackered.

'Fist me, lick me, fuck me, fist me, fist me, Anvar, right now.' This is how men must feel; if I say no I'm sure I will be sentenced to putting up shelves and not being allowed to go to the football for a month.

1.30am

Someone is shouting on us. Knocking on the door. It's Rachel. 'Come on you guys, you've been down here over an hour.'

Anya's still screaming. I've taken to whimpering on the floor. So drunk and facially numb I think I've left my tongue in there.

Notice Anya properly. Blue satin bra and pants. Hairy armpits, legs, and a greedier cunt than my own.

Now it's my turn.

'No Anvar, we better go up.'

2.20am

Some Indian geezer takes my number. Well, everyone else has it.

3am

Champagne. Rachel is explaining that she lets Anya fuck who she wants as long as she doesn't see that woman again. Anya explains that she lets Rachel fuck who she wants but as long as she approves of her choice.

Apparently they both agreed the moment they saw me that I'm completely useable.

Anya slips her email address on a napkin into my jeans pocket. Isn't anyone faithful nowadays?

2pm

Wake up. Was last night real? If it is, my life is one bad dream. Find email address in back pocket. Find a man's number and name.

To some people my life may seem like a rollercoaster, but to me, it feels more like being on a tram because wild rides now seem as mundane as a journey to work.

10pm

Decide Nigel isn't quite a sociopath. Just a troubled man, with as many lives in his back pocket as a serial killer has bodies under his floorboards.

10.45pm

Ding Dong. A text. From Nigel. This is what I get for being compassionate. I am just begging the heavens to take the piss.

How r u? Nx

This is surreal. Bugger off.

12.20am

Sitting on end of bed, talking to myself, thinking – Anvar, don't give away your trust. And all women should accept that it's the last thing you should hand over. A man has to prove he is worthy of that much more than he has to prove he is worthy of your love, because that's the easy part.

19 March

Wake up. It's 4pm. Been hitting the bottle. Sleep. Wake up. Throw up. Back to bed. Moby's going off. Always, always ringing. Where is the moby? Maybe an agent. Could be wondering where I am. Maybe missed a real big job, and will now never be famous.

Stop ringing! Oh. Pain from the back of my head down to my ass. Is it a sex injury? Have I been having sex? No, no. Only remember going to Budgens and back. That's right. The guy from upstairs came to the door. About the noise. Said he'd been waiting all week for *Auf Wiedersehen Pet* and couldn't hear his telly. Will send him a bunch of roses or something. Hungry. Waddle to fridge. Nothing in it. Close door. Huh? Open door. See phone on top shelf. Close fridge door. Think. Open fridge door. Answer moby. Weird Japanese voice. Distant recollection of that voice . . . end call. Crawl to bedroom. Fall asleep on a pillow under the bed.

20 March

Thinking of going into therapy.

21 March

1pm

Three calls from Nigel already today. I ignore them. Column this week for the Scottish *News of the World*: How You Know When A Man Is A Cheat.

2pm

Three more calls from Nigel.

4pm

Time to knock this on the head.

6.15pm

Call Nigel, phone goes to voicemail, of course.

'Hi Nigel, it's Anvar here. Know you must be busy, what with travelling all over the country, attending meetings, and turning up at appointments your secretary has notified you of by fax. I'm fine. Really cool but you know, my frenzied and successful media career means I get a bit tired and jaded, you know, and I was wondering, seeing as you're the boss, if you could get some time off and we could travel a bit. Oh Nigel, I can see it now! Two first-class tickets to New York, a three-month residency at the Dorchester, where I could write my book, oh! Bliss! They have a really good spa there. And, Nigel, some spending money for Tiffanys. Well, I am a girl! Or, I know Nigel! Forget about BA! You could charter your private plane yourself. Nigel, this is the best idea I've had for ages! I am SO excited. And then you could show me and my girlfriends around your pad in the Hamptons. You do have a home there don't you? Where we could stay. And use as a holiday home, as you have so many homes, Nigel, you could spare one, surely. Call me.'

7.28pm

Nigel is calling. Let it go to voicemail. Dial answering machine.

'Anvar, I know you don't want to see me again, I get the message, I know we're over, I'm not stupid you know, I know what you're saying, but I'm a gentleman, and if you ever need a plane, there's a jet on stand-by waiting for you.'

Mate, you fucking psycho.

How To Sleep With A Gay Man And Seduce Him Afterwards

8pm

Ramone is over at mine with his mate Brian. They brought chocolate digestives and some garlic bread that they argued over in the supermarket. They are staying for dinner.

Brian asks to see my wardrobe while Ramone stirs the chilli and shouts about how little parsley there is on the baguettes. Ramone thinks he and Brian should have gone to Tesco.

Show Brian my favourite dress and he helps me put it on. Brian is really rather attractive, with dark hair and a square jaw and tattoos. As he adjusts my bra strap, I feel a shiver, his touch is gentle, and the moment is ruined as Ramone yells through to us that my rice-cooker has seen better days.

Brian has been 'out' for fifteen years and admits to me he misses women's 'tits'.

I just love how men can be so open and honest with me and I mean that most insincerely.

When I feign surprise at his confession, Brian says all gay men have a 'fascination' with breasts. The big, buxom kind, the Disneyesque fullness of large page 3 mountains.

I see.

Men are no longer chasing mammoths, but are after mammoth mammories instead.

Brian is a stylist and says I could do more with my own cleavage. I say I do. Push up, push apart, flatten or just hang au naturel, there's loads a girl can do with her treasure chest.

For a laugh Brian puts on my tuxedo and my Sandeman hat. He strikes a very Prince pose in front of my full-length mirror, hands on hips, head turned slightly, legs straight, cheeks tight. He has a whiff of the heterosexual about him.

PRETTY WILD

10pm

Ramone leaves to meet a friend. Brian wants to give me a makeover. I open a bottle of bubbly. This is fun. He carefully selects shades of blusher and eyeshadow by holding the palettes up to my skin and eyes. He smiles at me warmly. I feel cosily attracted to him, the same draw you feel towards your hairdresser, masseur or any man who can relax you and attend to you, the Dr Feelgoods of our world.

11.30pm

Both yawning. Brian wants to paint my toenails. I agree. Decide better to do them when I'm lying on bed. Am purring. Mentions he's missed his last bus home to Notting Hill. I say he can crash here.

Asks me if I want to party a little. Pulls out poppers from his bag. I laugh, say I've never tried them before. I inhale, splutter, panic, as if I'm being dragged down under the water by a dead weight. Then I surface and giggle. Brian is watching me, bemused.

'Do you want to feel them?' I'm asking. Crazy with power.

'What?'

'My breasts,' I'm saying. I take his hand and press it onto my chest.

'I've never done it with a woman before.'

Whoa!

Guys can't do affection, they think it's foreplay.

'It's alright, we don't have to do anything, Brian.'

'I don't know if I can,' he says as I pull him down to the mattress.

He's more attentive to my tits than any heterosexual lover has been before. All night. Snogging, stroking and nestling. Feel like a pagan goddess, throwing up my femininity as something benign and comforting.

Well, it is Mother's Day.

22 March

At 9am Brian stumbles out of my flat, red-faced – murmuring 'it was lovely and I'll call you'. Aye, right.

Fridge Magnet Philosophy:
Men, the more you turn, the less you learn.

1 April

April Fool's Day, only for those who don't feel foolish enough already.

2 April

On a train to Sheffield to see Anna. Phone goes. It's Kelvin.

'Anvar I'm at home alone, where are you, you sexy girl?'

'On a train.' Sitting opposite an elderly woman who is drinking coffee and reading an Aga saga.

'I'm in my bedroom, and guess what I've got?'

'No idea.'

'A hard on, and who is it for?'

Looking at the pensioner, she seems happy. Wonder if she was ever plagued by almost married erotomaniacs when she was young. Think my sexual adventures are not common to any other woman than me. Take a few seconds to worry about that.

'I'm on a train, Kelvin.'

'Okay, will it be a, b, or c?'

'I'm not up for this Kelvin. I think you should stop calling me.'

Aga saga woman has stopped reading and is staring at me.

'Anvar, I was looking at a new catalogue the other day and they have some very nice pieces from Italy, exceptional quality, and I . . .'

'I don't want any more underwear Kelvin.'

Not ever. People usually sell their soul to the devil for a bigger reward than a few lousy pieces of silk.

'Anvar, you can't be serious?'

'Yes I am. Stop stalking me Kelvin. Or I'll tell your partner you've been harassing me.'

'You wouldn't do that?'

'Try me.'

My fellow passenger has stopped sipping her coffee, stopped reading her book, and has effectively ground to a halt.

'Bye.' Hang up. Look out window. Realise a few members of the public are staring at me. Think it's because I'm wearing a glitter boob tube on a rainy day. Never occurs to me it's because my life sounds weird.

5 April

Kelvin calls and leaves a message saying he needs 'closure'. I thought hanging up on him would make him realise it was over but he's such a phone junkie that ending it means having some skin sex. I am just so in the wrong movie.

12 April

Voicemail from a woman who says she's called Madam Titubana. At least think that's what she said. Has a very thick Japanese accent. Says she might have some work for me, if I'm interested. Says she's been trying to contact me for ages.

Think she must be a nutter who's read some of my columns, and wants to put me in some dodgy documentary. I mean, that I can do myself.

Sure she says something about a 'Dom'. Don't know him. Perhaps she means 'condom'. Why would anyone call me to talk about contraception? Maybe the Family Planning want me as a mascot.

Can't believe I have to spend five minutes of my life thinking about this shite. I mean, I have a facial to get to.

Maybe she means 'dom' as in dominant, maybe she's a sadist. Wonder if I should call the police. Can see the headline now. 'Columnist found in dungeon shocker'. Only if I'm wielding the whip, boys; that would be a dream job and somewhat great for PMT.

20 April
7pm

At a press launch for a new magazine. The editor is rather tasty. Quite blindingly raunchy and very charismatic; the nearest I've ever got to feeling some sexual electricity that's not connected to my Rabbit.

Inveigle his company. Slink into his conversation. Flirt with him under the pretence of wanting to write features for him, which I wouldn't because his rag is between *Kerrang!* and *Readers Wives* and I only sink that low when I'm high.

He's really interesting. Smart guy. Laugh loads. Invites me for dinner. Expensive wine. Back to his flash pad in London Bridge. Champagne. A slow dance to Amy Winehouse. More champagne. He runs me a bubble bath. An erotic massage with exotic oil he brought back from Egypt. Luscious. Get a bit rock 'n' roll. Put on Queens of the Stone Age. He smokes some weed. I do my victory dance for him; roll my wrists and flop my fingers with my arms above my head, a Bollywood princess having a fit, shaking my arse like Baloo from *The Jungle Book*. Well, I think I look sexy.

Fling myself against the wall, and go splat. Recover my dignity to gyrate up and down it. Amazing what you can do when there's a partition to hold you up.

Flop onto the couch. Done my bit.

Masterful man this. Grabs me and turns me over. We're

fucking on the sofa, like dogs, he's taking me from behind.

Thirty seconds in. Then I hear it.

'Phwoarrrrrtt.'

He keeps going. Must have imagined it.

'PHWOARRRTT.'

He's stopping.

'No keep going Giles, please.'

We compose ourselves, and we are getting it on, big time, oh yes. Oh no.

'PHWOARRTT!'

'I'm really sorry,' I say.

'It's fine.'

Okay, so we're slowly getting back on track here and I'm really trying to squeeze those kegels and yet I feel like I'm working a pair of bellows.

'PHWOARRTT!!'

Enough. He's pulling out, the troops are going right back home.

'I'm sorry,' I'm saying. 'Think I drank too much beer today.'

He looks bemused.

'This has really never, ever happened to me before,' I say.

It hasn't. Telling the truth. I've heard men joke about fanny farts but I've never had an attack. Ever. It just doesn't stop. I'm sitting here and they're still burbling out of me.

'Do you want to go again?' I'm asking.

'Let's have a drink,' he's saying.

Go for a pee, sit on the pan and stare down at my little purse amazed and horrified at its treachery. Not so much backdraft as frontdraft.

Its breach of the peace. Its uncouth bad manners. How can it do this to me? There's some kind of air balloon up there.

Walk back into lounge. Sit elegantly on sofa. Cross legs. Mistake.

'Phwoarrtt.'

Giles is looking through his diary. 'I've got an early tomorrow, Anvar, so can I call you a taxi?'

21 April

Fanny flatulence, that's what I have. Don't know how I contracted it. I fear I may never shag again. You just can't, knowing that will happen.

The shame of it. Am mortified. That's my sex life over. Done. Finito. I am Ms Farting Flaps. Can't expect a man to live with that. Not even one who loves you.

To add insult to injury, have artex burns on my ass from grinding against the wall of his flat.

Don't think he'll call; if he does it will only be to recommend a gynaecologist.

27 April
6pm

Go for drinks with Barclay, a TV researcher who's working on ideas with me.

'I've been doing some sensible shopping this morning. A frying pan for £4.99. I'm not the kind of person who will spend £150 on a whole set of things. I got a garlic crusher last week, which I'm quite pleased with, and oh, a nice knife for the vegetables.'

Barclay's in a relationship.

'I got fed up waking up beside some strange woman, got fed up being drunk, if I'm not attached I just press the self-destruct button and off I go. We all get older Anvar. I just wanted to give it all up and move to the country and have a couple of kids and a Labrador.'

Barclay's very settled in his life now.

'I have it all. A beautiful wife, stunning, well-adjusted children, a garden, and we've nearly paid off the mortgage.'

RADIO TAXIS

(SOUTHAMPTON) LTD.

NO BOUNDARY CHARGES

(023)80 666 666

24 HOUR SERVICE

Find us @ www.radtax.co.uk

OR 0800 666 666

DRIVER RECEIPT/CREDIT CARD & JOB RECORD PAD

Passenger .... Car Code No. 179

From ....

To ....

....

Cost of Journey 6 · 00 Date 09, 10, 09 Time ......:......

Credit Card No. *(last four digits)* ....

Expiry Date........................... Issue No. ....

Card Holder's Signature ....

Driver's Signature ....

This is not a VAT receipt - (the driver is not registered)

9pm

Lying on my bed laughing hysterically. Heee heee hee, ho ho ho. I'm rasping. Have now reached a high-pitched 'eeeee, eeee'. My stomach muscles feel like they're bruised.

Weak with mirth. Lie on my stomach, rubbing my belly. Catch my breath.

People still believe in the whole country house bollocks thingummy. Fools. Panting. Look around at my flat. The sight of a little bag of shopping with its little loaf of bread, for a small single person moves me uncontrollably. Burst into tears. Lie weeping on bed. Fall asleep on top of the duvet. Wake up at dawn and roll it over me so I look like a human sausage. Lie very still and stare at the cornicing.

30 April

7pm

For some reason think I need to make reparation to Giles. Discuss this with Anna. Do not mention the fanny farts. Think this information is prejudicial and out of the context of the main question which is whether I should call him. First. As he has not called me. Which is understandable. However.

'Do you think I should text him and say, "hi, just a quickie, hope all is well with you, give us a phone sometime, say Monday", or is that too pushy?'

'Well, I . . .' Anna's saying.

'Or what if I text and say, hi, dinner's on me, say Tuesday? Or does that make me sound desperate?'

'Thing is Anvar . . .'

'I mean why hasn't he texted? Do you think he's busy?'

'He may well be but . . .'

'Or what if I'm more casual and say, I'm in Soho on Wednesday, at Soho House, if you're going to be there, call me and I'll buy you a drink? Simple, huh?'

'You could, Anvar, I suppose but . . .'

'Maybe I should just be honest, I mean, life is short, you've got to say what you want to say! What's wrong with being forthright. That's who I am! That's me, for God's sake. Me! ME! Why should I hide it? I think, I should put all my cards on the table, and say, look I fancy you, you fancy me, let's get together. Say Thursday? If he says no, he says no, that's it, at least I know where I stand.'

A sudden quiet descends. Hate when she does that. Know I'm going AWOL when her pregnant pauses turn into abortive silences.

'But he's never texted you.' Anna is losing patience I can tell.

'Right, that's it, I'm not going to text him at all. Never. Just see what happens, forget it, get on with my life. You are right. I'll look too keen and might fuck it all up.'

'We can't fuck up if we don't do anything,' Anna concludes.

Feel bowled over by the profundity of this statement.

2 May

Anna sends me an email.

> Anvar, I think you are so right not to call Giles. Okay he might seem like the best thing to have happened to you for a while as he is not, it seems, a liar, a freak, or a bastard psycho, indeed he seems nice and successful and a man with taste. It seems a shame that you've met a guy you can get on with and it's screwing up already.
> However, I think you have to be cautious and definitely ignore him.
> I'm learning that men are really different, and relationships are difficult because you need so much patience.
> Men like to make the moves and feel they are in control of how the relationship is developing; that's why we have to let

them do the chasing, not because we are wussy, who can't go after what we want, but because men need to feel in charge. Especially if they think you might mean a great deal to them. You have to stay out their face you have to let them miss you. This is what I've learned and I share it with you. Hope this helps. Love you.

PS Don't call him. Let him come to YOU.

4 May
3pm
No call. Giles is not missing me.

6pm
Kinda pished. Drinking red wine on an empty stomach. Keep wanting to pick up the phone. Trigger-happy fingers. Stick a post-it note on the telephone landline saying 'No!'.

8pm
Put an A4 page on the bathroom wall saying 'Never call a man before he calls you'. Decide I might not read it often enough. Stick another A4 page with 'Don't call him!' in big letters on my TV screen.

10.22pm
Hi giles, hope ur well, give us a call and see if we can do next week, say fri? Anvar xxxxxxxxxxxxxxxxxxxxxxxxxxxxxxxxxxxxx

It's 11.07pm – the cunt, the shit, the ignorant fucking arsehole.

12.10am
He definitely does not want to see or even hear me again. I know that if a man doesn't call it's because he doesn't want to.

Simple. I feel so mad with it all!

I am not destined to have any personal happiness. You couldn't send me any more signs about this, it's written in the stars, it's in neon, it's practically a tattoo.

If a man doesn't want a relationship you're fighting something you can't see.

Huh. It's all bullshit. I figure that no one deserves love. We all think we do but we don't. It's talked about like it's a reward for all the shit and pain in life; for every man who lied, for every call you expected that never materialised, yes, you are supposed to meet the right person as if it's the pay-off, like enduring so you get to heaven. Me thinking like this is disabling and treacherous because you should be strong without a man. I think I probably am, but still feel like a pack of hounds have all taken a chunk of me.

12.30am

I'm slipping. NOTHING EVER WORKS OUT!

Fed up being let down, confused, hurt, disappointed, clueless.

Buy litre of vodka, and a party bag of ice from late nite grocers. Start drinking.

3am

Rehearsing a dance routine in the living room for an appearance on TOTP as Debbie Harry's backing vocalist.

4am

Am Debbie Harry.

6am

Zzzzzz . . .

7.15am

I've woken up. Fully clothed. Look at my gear. Realise that I never, ever really like what I'm wearing.

PRETTY WILD

9am

Amazed I'm still alive. One day I won't wake up. I know it. I'll pass away gently to that big cocktail bar in the sky. Think about writing a poem called 'Ode To My Liver'.

9.01am

Really pissed still. La la la la la la. Experiencing Vietnam type flashbacks to previous poems. When my sandwich left me, God I really missed it, that was until I found solace with my rich tea biscuit. Wrote that for a laugh once.

9.02am

Realise I'm deeply weird.

10am

Think I'm feeling braver. That, or I'm numb with vodka.

Still, there's always two ways of looking at stuff. If you prepare for a decade or two of being married and having kids and it never happens you have a huge chunk of life to spend on your own like a big fat lottery cheque. So it figures you have to be inventive and be somewhat of an artist about how you design those years. I mean, that's a lotta space to fill and you gotta be a big person to do it.

The 24-Hour Relationship

6 May
6pm
Another Islington barbecue. This time at Biff's house – he's another ex-pat like me.

Eating berries out a tub, devouring cocktails. Realise I haven't taken my dark glasses off for a month. I'm in mourning for the men who came, the men who left and the ones who outstayed their welcome.

Is that? No way. It is! It's that guy, whatsisname, the one who used to live in Glasgow, about the West End, it is! Recognise the green snakey eyes. Hello! Craig? It's me, Anvar. Oh yeah in those days I wore doc martins and a scowl. Terrible life. Poor. Ate nothing but pot noodles on toast. It showed, yeah. Love *Vogue* magazine now.

What you doin' here? Moved down ten years ago? Really? Wow. Really wow yeah. Did you not run off with a band or something?

A lost weekend? Darling, my lost weekend has gone on for a few years now. No I'm not blind it's the glare of daylight you know, far too sunny down here, hurts the old cornea. They're vintage Ferragamo, yeah. No, never take them off. Yes, sleep with them on sometimes too, well, I don't have curtains in the bedroom. I look like a pop star? No, surely not. Moi? You are so sweet. Can I sit down?

7pm
Being filled in on Craig's life. 'Thing is Anvar, I can't remember much between 1990 and now. Whatever year it is.'

He is so rock 'n' roll. Nine lifetimes on the road this guy, with assorted fucked-up and junkie rock legends. Quite nice to find this kind of seedy glamour in a bourgeois part of central London where a good night out is seeing a French film with subtitles.

8pm

Am getting more and more inebriated, catching parts of Craig's chat. He's travelled. 'Women in America, blow jobs must have been on the syllabus. God they can suck cock. I got my cock sucked for a ticket for a rock concert, y'know, and do you know what? There were plenty tickets left.'

'No. Really? That is just SO interesting. I could write a column about that, I really could. Wow. Yeah.'

8.30pm

Am gruesomely fascinated. Craig's been to places in countries where his addictions forced him to enter sleazy, parasitical partnerships.

'Of course I've slept with boys. You've slept with girlies haven't you? How did you find it? It doesn't do it for me, I'm afraid. I did it for a fix, or just food, depending on how hard up I was at the time.'

'That's just so liberating,' I say. I am SO making an arse of myself.

9pm

Craig's married, another gesture in his spiralling journey towards self-annihilation.

'We were just junkies together. She saved me once and I saved her. Lying on the bathroom floor unconscious. I don't know where my wife is. She's probably dead. Shit happens.'

'Jesus, you have really seen and done it all. Wow.'

9.03pm

Saw it. That look. When he was talking. His eyes kept meeting my cleavage.

10pm

He is spellbinding. I am titillated, but not as much as he wants to be. I'm a 34F cup and a size 12 in jeans; an Asian Dolly Parton but without her gravitas. I'm sexy, fuckable, yet I am not on the inside what appears to the naked eye.

I have sometimes felt so trapped in this Disney cartoon of a body that I feel like writing to Stephen Hawking and telling him how much I empathise with how he must feel. I have a mind too. People are so judgemental.

11pm

Think it's time I tried a guy who's actually seems really fucked up, as opposed to a man who appears to be normal and who is actually and extremely and inordinately fucked up inside.

11.30pm

This is a man who does not mince his words.

'Come on Anvar, let's get dirty. You know you want to.'

Huh! I am shocked. You just can't say things like that to me. This is scandalous! Okay, you can say things like that to me, but I can't let him think I am not completely taken aback.

And anyway, think, Anvar, think. This guy's had a really dodgy past. Okay, so we all you know you like a bit of rough, but really! And we know you like a man to be bad. So, what you waiting for? Here he is! A big present and all for you!

The weird thing is, as well, I used to fancy him years ago, and now, well, the forces of fate have combined to throw us together again. This is remarkable! Good work Mistress Destiny.

However . . . he's been very clear about his history. There's no way I'd ever risk my health having sex, my mental and emotional health possibly, but those are easily fixed with a detox and a holiday.

No. Thinking about the druggie bit. An unscrupulously charming past yes, but I have a future, somewhere, and maybe with someone. I gotta take care of what hasn't happened to me yet, just in case it does.

'Craig. Fine offer. Really flattered thanks. And I'd love to get dirty with you, as you say. But. Thing is. I'm HIV negative and I intend to stay that way. That's it! I'm being honest. You'll have to chap on Biff's door and ask him if he's got a spare condom.'

Craig doesn't look that offended. Well, what would offend him? A cucumber sandwich and Earl Grey tea, something normal like that? Or asking him to put his glass of vodka on a coaster?

Huh. He's laughing. Doing that snorting yet tickled thing that men do when they think you are being sweetly dim.

'Anvar, I can't ask him that! What am I supposed to say, hey mate, any spare rubbers lying around, me and Anvar are downstairs wanting to get on with it?'

There's no reason to make out I'm being impractical when I'm being incredibly practical. I'm doing this for us.

I am miffed. 'Why not. He'll understand. He's a guy isn't he?' Hold on. Biff's the man who asks us to take our shoes off when we come to his house. Mine are languishing at the front door and their absence has just made me four inches smaller.

Guess the man who doesn't want dirty feet on his precious carpet might not want random acts of filth explored on it either.

'We don't have to go that far, you know that,' he says.

'S'pose.'

'You know that we need a condom. Anvar. We're both adults, we know we can do other things,' he states.

12 midnight

Mad intense snogging. I'm in experienced hands. He's a fuck machine.

12.25am

Oh whoah woooo!!! And we are hungry for each other. How lovely.

And I am naked and we're on.

I know he's turning me on but I do feel a bit woozy. I never usually take weed, yet think that wee smoke I had earlier, well, it's really messing me up right now.

Getting paranoid. And I have the munchies. Think then that all I eat will poison me.

Oh, he's pressing his thumb on my wee asshole.

Oh God, I hope he doesn't think we are going to do THAT!

Craig was really okay about the condom thang.

I can trust him, sure I can, he was a nice guy years ago and still is I know.

Thing is . . . if he was a heroin addict, well, what was that article again?

'Oh, Craig, don't bite me there, thanks.'

Yeah, it was all about the toll being an addict takes on your body. And they were handing out advice.

Partners of addicts who have erection problems are encouraged to stroke their bodies in a non-sexual and sensual way.

I call that the soft option. Well, it is.

I've never sure about touching a man in a non-sexual way. It's never worked for me, never mind them. That sort of platonic stuff is for your father, brother and girlfriends' husband's.

Oh, he has a gorgeous chest! Hairy and lived in. A few stray whites and greys.

You know . . . I could be being way out and fucked up in the head, what with that smoke, but, Craig might be wimping out of doing the full monty, because well, he can't.

12.49am
'STOP!'

He's jumping up. Looks frightened.

'What is it Anvar?'

'I need a cuddle.'

Okay, okay, can't think of how else to stop him. Stop us.

He spreads a sleeping bag on the floor. 'Not what we were looking for but it'll do.' Beckons me over and I lie down beside him doing my best impersonation of a woman in emotional crisis.

'So did you inject or smoke crack?' I ask casually, in my squeakiest, babiest voice.

'Smoked it.'

'Is that nice?' I'm asking, concerned.

'It's not especially nicer – just gets the job done.'

'Did you ever share bongs?' I'm persisting, worrying that there might be some chance of Hep B, C or fucking Z in the communality of its digestion.

Craig is looking at me queerly. 'No. Music?'

He's choosing a CD on the laptop. The dub Asian sounds of Muslim calls to prayer and bhangra bass emanate from the stadium speakers. I have to say I'm a bit freaked out.

'Is this music culturally significant in some way?' I start to wonder if all my lovers have some Bollywood soundtrack going off in their heads when they play with me.

'No.' He's kissing my neck. There's a six-month incubation period if you have HIV you know.

'When was the last time you had sex?' I ask.

He's working his mouth down towards my nipples.

'Months ago.'

'Right, we are definitely not doing it. Especially if you can't even ask your mate of fifteen years for a condom.'

1am

Back at mine.

He lets me put a finger up his asshole. He kisses me like an animal. He bites my nipples. He fists me while he says, 'You are the most stubborn, dominating, opinionated woman I've ever met and I am so impressed. I am going to enjoy breaking you in, Anvar. I'm going to have fun making you my sex slave.'

Hot and horny sex with a dash of perversion and the odd deviant flourish.

Now we are cooking.

My wrists are tied together with bondage tape. My ankles separated and bound by leather cuffs attached to a three-foot silver pole. He turns me over onto my knees and pushes the bar over my back until my feet sit on my buttocks. Then he fucks me from behind. All done in silence, I am the willing conspirator, there was nothing to be said.

Just as well, really, that I am speechless. He's fucking my mouth, touching the back of my throat with his cock, again and again, and now he's calling on Jesus Christ to help him. A lot of people seem to fuck Jesus Christ. They're always shouting for him in the bedroom.

7 May

2am

We take a break. Giggle like hyenas. Sex is so good it's a crying game.

3am

'I haven't laughed so much in years,' he's saying. 'You're a bit special, Anvar.'

3.30am

Off to 24-hour off sales. Need more bubbly. Need snacks. Craig in flat, waiting for me. Wow. I'm so sleepy.

Bread, yeah, chocolate, yeah, condoms, yeah, need many many more of them . . . Doritos yeah, tortilla chips, yeah, and some Wotsits, yeah, chewing gum, yeah, and some dolly mixtures, yeah, and some scouring sponges, yeah, need them, yeah, hope he likes all this? What if he doesn't? He's my guest. Better make it three bags of Doritos mate and one bag of Monster Munch, yeah, thanks, and milk, and some olives . . . oh, and 80 Marlboro, three bottles of cava and a tub of dairy ice cream please. Thanks very much.

3.40am

Walk into flat singing.

Go into bedroom happy as Santa with all my surprise treats. There's a note on my pillow. Strange. Where is his rucksack? Where is his bag! His coat! Shit. The room's spinning. He's done a runner. He's done a runner. He's GONE!

4am

Sitting, swaying on my couch, chain smoking. Feel very hurt. Such a shock. Never expected that at all.

Call him. On voicemail. Leave a message.

'Craig, can't believe you just got up and left like that. I mean, I've done that before, I guess, but you know it's shit, really shit of you and I hope you are okay and not ill or have been called away suddenly or summat . . . but this is the shittiest thing a guy has done to me for ages . . . well, most recently. Bye.'

4.30am

Remember there's a note. Read it. Don't understand the writing. Says something about needing air.

4.31am

Crash out.

10am

Doorbell is buzzing. Aaarrgghh! Oh my head. Oh my heart. Oh my pussy!

'Hi Anvar, it's Craig here.'

Let him in immediately.

'How are you this morning?' I ask, aware that I should have been pacing the floor all night worried about him but took a coma instead.

'Feeling a bit sheepish Anvar, to tell you the truth.' Oh baa-baa-baa.

'Really, why's that?' I ask as I collect my mail and walk upstairs to get back into my bed.

'Last night, I got a bit carried away.'

'Oh yeah?' I'm opening my letters.

'I'm sorry I fucked off,' he whined. 'You know, coke and all that.'

'Huh?'

'Mate called, said he had some gear, dashed off to meet him, collect it, and come back, I meant to come back to yours but, you know, it was good stuff and well I . . .'

Lord, there it was. He was screaming on the merry-go-round at the fair for all to see. He just couldn't leave the circus of psycho bambis and stoners.

'Craig,' I'm saying and I'm fucking angry. 'You had a choice; coke or me, and you chose coke. I don't like junkies.'

Oh Anvar, too harsh girl! That is outta order woman! On the other hand! Shouldn't be a great contest should it? The facts are unbearable; me lying naked in flagrante or a line or ten. Duh! What will I choose, he says, and he has to think about it!

It takes a lot to get off heroin, sure, and not much to get off with me, yet I think I'm the better habit.

'I better go. I'm sorry.'

4pm

Surveying the chaos of the room, the knocked-over cans, the spilled ashtrays, the vertical piles of videos now osmosing like a virus on the floor. Better clean up. I couldn't be caught in such a riot. Euch! Aprons and dusters ain't my style. I've never done it with Mr Sheen or Mr Muscle and they've never done it for me.

PRETTY WILD

5pm

You see I've never been out with a smackhead before. I presume they are like all men but perhaps less reliable, more poor, and definitely living with fewer memories than most of us. Huh. Am kinda jealous of that in a way. There are things we'd all like to forget we have done.

5.15pm

A rest. Head on pillow.

Thinking that Craig is at the same immature level as when he first got addicted, still stuck in that stasis.

He's had a decade of being nothing more than a man who needed a fix, and hunted down cash on a daily basis like a child seeking a Willy Wonka chocolate bar hiding the golden ticket to the factory. Sure, he may be 38, but in man years that makes him about 14.

If you spend your relationship years unconscious, instead of learning to love, it's a hell of a long time to be out of it, and you're not going to know the boundaries of what is acceptable, even when you like a girl.

5.30pm

I'm a normal girl. I have feelings sometimes. I'm always looking for the seven out of ten factor equation. If most things seem good and in place then let your guard down a little.

Mine should have stayed on sentry duty.

5.45pm

In a day, you are introduced to all aspects of the man; future problems shake your hand, idiosyncrasies wave, warning bells clank like the machinery of hell.

There's only one reason a man does not appear when he says he will; there's someone else.

6pm

Very exhausted. Early night I feel, and some nice food.
Ding! Dong! And it's a text! Oh no, from Craig.

Dear Anvar, There are a great many reasons I can't keep
seeing you. I don't hate you. But I really feel this isn't
working. You're great fun, honest and sexy but I'm just not
up for it. C x

PARDON?

6.05pm

Let me get this right. HE is chucking ME?

6.10pm

Never once in my slut career have I received a Mr Nice Guy
rejection letter complete with compliments. Am gazing at my
mobile. I realise I have excelled myself, and that warms me. At
least I'm making headway in something.

6.15pm

This is a full-scale public relations disaster. The fact of the
matter is that I've been expertly chucked by a man I never even
wanted a relationship with in the first place.
   Is this for real?
   I know not who I am anymore. We were only having casual
sex, for God's sake, now we are having casual text.

6.20pm

Gone are the days when you told a person face to face that you
didn't want them around anymore. Now you put it in writing
and press send.

6.30pm

Maybe the text is a pre-emptive strike, designed to overshoot any ideas of a romance. Huh.

Of course, you know what that means? You can't even have sport sex nowadays without being placated by guys who want to finish with you as respectfully as they would a long-term, lovelorn girlfriend.

I am in HELL! Everyone is mad!

I have no idea how I got here. I mean, I think I am in control.

7pm

Fuming. Bloody fuming.

7.18pm

Taking shit is a matter of choice; Craig didn't just want to see how much I could take in bed, he wanted to test how far he could push me for real.

7.25pm

Just occurs to me I spent a whole day with Craig. The whole thing was done and dusted from sunset to sunrise.

7.35pm

I'm a victim of the 24-hour relationship, the more adult and grown up version of a quickie, where apologies and exits more suited to saying goodbye to a partner are foisted upon women with no ambitions of men other than getting laid. Where the highs, lows, pain and disappointments of an affair are crammed into a day. Men have created the 24-hour relationship, along with guns, war, X-boxes and the Playstation.

It exists for them and them alone.

8pm

I'm looking at the words again. There are 'a great many reasons why I can't keep seeing you'.

Craig thinks he's denying himself sex with me out of some knightly code, but really he wanted in a lover a woman who was a little more manageable.

Yep, he has another woman.

8.15pm

Am gutted. Tired. Still trying to get to grips with this mess. And it is a mess.

Surely all this chaos isn't necessary, just to have some sex?

Think the problem with the 24-hour relationship is that it straddles ever so tenderly what can be dismissed as a sex thing and what has the potential to be a full-on thing.

Maybe that's what the text was about; men wanting to leave every raw situation where you were vulnerable, believing they are still a nice guy, as if you can remedy the horror of what has gone before in the manner of the dumping.

In the world of sex and relationships, permanent bewilderment is inevitable.

Being single is either a lifestyle choice or the refuge of the cynic and the hurting. No big surprise then, that marriage happens in panic, and love may not happen at all.

9pm

Bath. Bed. And perhaps some bad dreams.

Once upon a time we had fairy tales to keep us informed of our inevitable union, now we have predictatext to annoy and disappoint us.

8 May

3pm

Spot Craig on Upper Street. He's with a girl. She looks like she owns him, has her arms wrapped around him, leaning into his chest. They ain't just met.

4pm

Call Craig. And he answers.

'Hi Anvar, you get my text?'

'Are you seeing anyone?' I ask. Silence.

'Yes, I am, never told you a lie.'

4.01pm

It wasn't enough that he fucked me, he had to fuck me over too.

Men are strange creatures; they have a twisted notion of truth. Not revealing themselves is their idea of honesty. He might have thought that by omitting certain facts there was an honour in his whoredom. I, however, do not.

'Why me?' I shout out of curiousity.

'When I saw you I saw something I wanted.'

'And her?'

'I forgot.'

'You forgot about her?'

Hey, his girlfriend and most of his life; yep, he did say he couldn't remember much.

Even when you are strong they still manage through their own peculiar genius to do you some wrong.

7pm

Thinking of writing a book called *How To Spot A Bastard*. That'd sell.

Thought I'd earned my stripes.

Unfaithful men must be the norm, they can't all have been making an exception for me.

7.05pm

Am amazed at the serendipity of it all.

I am aghast that history repeats itself even when you are sorted and have moved on.

Men and their rotten natures even fly in the face of coincidence.

7.10pm

Just because you want to shag men for your own sexual gratification, does not mean they have the right to deal you crap.

If men can dupe us into this degree of security, then you may end up being one of those poor mares who award a man twenty years of their life to discover he's been screwing around.

9pm

A text from Sam, dear Sam, the one I faked an orgasm with. My male pal I seduced on a night out when I was bored, and all because I knew he always had a thing about me. I am such a user. He's makes a huge effort to reassure me he's still on my side. All these supportive texts every few months. Go on Anvar. Think about this. Here's a single man, who is decent towards women and respectful of us, and you fucked him over by pretending that you fancied him and that he was turning you on. He didn't deserve that. Bitch.

Here goes:

Sam, hi, thnx for this text, yes, am cool and yes, life is exciting in the big smoke, and im sorry ive not been in touch. I value our friendship 2, and i want you to know that I think u are an amazing guy and a guy im proud to call my friend. will c u when I get up to Glasgow. Ax

I am making my peace with Sam. If I do not, I fear I may become a man-hater, and even love will not be able to redeem me. There are some men who are nice, true and honest. Sam is my sole reminder of this. If I continue to shit on him then I am lost.

Why Every Woman
Is A Dominatrix These Days

9 May
1pm

Sunny. Go out for a walk. Grab a sandwich. Eat on the hoof. Stare into the window of Whistles. Make myself move on.

The weather is windy with sunny flashes, the traffic is as lethargic as an obese American. All cool.

'OI! IS THAT ANAWAR!'

Here I am, out and about, hunting down eats for dinner and I'm all calm and fairly jolly and now I have to listen to some crazy on the moby.

'Sorry, who's this? And by the way it's Anvar.'

'THIS IS MADAM TITUBANA! YOU WANT WORK? YOU WANNA BE DOM?'

Hmmm . . . the voice is familiar.

'Can I call you back?'

'Ho-kay.'

1.10pm

'Ramone?'

'Hey Anvar.'

'Ramone, do you know a woman called Madam Titubana?'

'Yes, oh, has she called? How exciting. Yes, I told her all about you,' Ramone's saying.

'And what precisely was that?'

'Anvar, she's got a job going. I just thought you'd be really interested. She's a dominatrix. And she needs an assistant, and I just thought, oh well, what does the job involve? So I asked her about it and she says she just needs some company in the dungeon, and it would have to be a woman and someone who won't get upset about what's going on and I said, oh, I know a woman like that and I gave her your number.'

'You did what?'

Ramone thinks I will be very good at this wee p/t job.

'It's important not to care about men, to be a Dominatrix,' he's saying. 'And you don't.'

3pm

Go to a café. Order panini. Think seriously about job offer.

A Dominatrix huh? Great thing to have on your CV.

Guess she is still a scary woman figure. And it's a great look, all those buckles and leather and shiny pvc. And the thigh-length boots are to die for.

Yes, I'd love a refill, thanks. Coffee. Yeah.

The Dominatrix. In control. Vicious. Uninvolved.

Her female power has been driven underground, and underground culture is always the sexiest.

You know, I think I will give it a go.

Soon all women who want to appear at ease with their sexuality, and who want to expose it in order to make some career move, will all be saying they were a dominatrix. The vocation is being numbed now, as common as being a porn star and going into politics.

Might as well jump on the bandwagon when the bandwagon is leaving town.

5pm

Call Madam Titubana.

'Hi, it's Anvar here.'

'Aha. You interested in being Dom?'

'Yeah. I think so. I'm strapped for cash, as they say, or you may say, huh! Yeah. Errmm . . . anyway, I think I should do it, I mean I write about these things, you know, sexual matters, and yep, I quite fancy doing it for real.'

'I get £300 you get £60.'

'Well, I was expecting more.'

'You amateur. Me professional.'

'Okay. But make it £80.'

'Ho-kay. Call you back please, have client now.'

6pm

Still feel reasonably interested in the proposition.

I have learned that it's probably better to rule men by fear.

They should be too scared to come near you.

Intimidation and terror is all men ultimately respect in their fucked-up, aggressive world.

Yep, well up for it. It almost seems terribly natural, a continuation of my loathing of the opposite sex.

A choker, a masque, a basque, thigh-high winkle-picker leather patent boots, this is the graduation outfit of any woman who has spent years studying men, because if you have you can only conclude that they are weak. And probably deserve a little humiliation, to keep them in their place.

7pm

Food shopping. Choosing dinner. Oh, it's Madam Titubana.

'YOU LIKE MEN OR ARE YOU GAY?' she's shouting.

'Sure, I like men. I sleep with them don't I?'

'YES, BUT VERY IMPORTANT NOT BECOME EMOTIONALLY INVOLVED! OI! CLIENTS VERY RICH GOOD LOOKING.'

'I'm not going to fall for a man who likes being chained up all the time!' I counter. 'If I wanted a pet I'd get a dog.'

'YOU LIKE DOGS?'

'No, I never said that.'

'HOW MANY MEN YOU SHAG?'

'I dunno. I've slept with, say, well, actually I can't recall.'

'YOU FANCY EM?'

She's stopped me in my tracks. She's got me. 'No, I don't have to fancy a man to sleep with him.'

The lassie working the till is looking at me strangely.

'LOOK MADAM TITUBANA.' I'm shouting now. 'I'M IN A FRUIT AND VEGETABLE SHOP. I CAN'T TALK.' The till girl hurls me a filthy as I abandon my full basket and run down a nearby lane.

'You use fruit and vegetables?' asks Madam Titubana. 'What vegetables? We more hardcore than that.'

'Why you asking me these questions?' I question, adopting her turn of phrase, missing out all pronouns and abbreviations, and not wanting to take her up on the 20 things you can do with a carrot. You mean, dear reader, you don't know?

'My work, how you say, specialised,' she tells me. 'Not professional to cry. Clients don't like squeamish.'

'I'll be fine.'

Jeez. On the strength of not being a girl who'll get easily upset at the horrors of pain inflicted in the dungeon, I am now hired as Madam Titubana's right-hand woman.

'Client wants tied up, whipped, spanked, I chain him this way, that way, I put him in a cage, I hang him upside down, I put him on a wheel. Yawn, yawn. Same old same old. Been doing this long time, 20 years, very boring for me. I need company, I need new ideas. Clients they always quiet because they, you know, gagged. Very boring for me. You work with me then me have someone talk to.'

Anvar, do not waver, be a sister. Madam Titubana is lonely. You have got to help her.

'You come to Great Portland Street tonight. Yes? WEAR SOMETHING DOM! HO-KAY?'

9pm
Back home. Thinking.

Being a dominatrix will be interesting, although it's not as subversive as it once was. It has become a modern, feminist job for any gal with a touch of anger. You're in control. Clients don't get to touch you; they take orders, they want punishment.

Everyone wants to be part of the sex industry. It's cool, gives you street cred.

But while ten-a-penny lapdancers strip off to support their university fees, or declare their past as a means to snagging a TV job or a centrefold shot, the dominatrix stands proud. Next to her, a lapdancer is Marks & Spencer lingerie. Palatable, nearly sexy and always nice.

Yet lapdancers are pussies, wimps. Brown-nosing men. Dancing for a bit of attention. Hoping for a big tip if they are asked to sit down for some banter. We're not so pretty. We're not so desperate. The client does what we want. He pays to experience woman in her most dogged, violent and cynical state.

Stuff kickboxing or weight-lifting or any sport that women adopt to declare their physical equality to men. You only compete with men if you mistakenly think they are superior. The dominatrix assumes her rightful position as the sex goddess. The sorceress. The boss.

10pm

Right Anvar, get ready!

Don't want to let her down.

I mean, I'm a perfectionist, like most imperfect people.

Hmm.

Okay. Let's empty this drawer onto the bed. I see. Thought I had more bits and pieces than this. Here it is. An assortment of belts, buckles, wristbands, g-strings, transparent bodies, lacy garters, and I think I will settle on a pair of red pvc gloves, suspenders, a plunge bra in black satin, accessorised with a set of handcuffs hanging from my thong, Betty Boop shoes, and the proverbial stockings. Oh, and a gold bling chain around my neck from Versace.

All in all, it is more than I usually wear full stop.

Shit. Don't have enough money to get a taxi. Shit. Now what? Go on the tube dressed like this?

10.10pm

They are looking at me, everyone is looking at me, they know what I'm doing, they know what I'm away to do. Switch off Khan. Think about this Dom thing again. I mean, I can turn back.

But that's being chicken. It will be really good research.

It's not a great indictment of men's sexuality, or the way they can view women as objects they can procure and have the right to buy.

But this male client I'm seeing tonight, he could be a nice guy.

Here I am, travelling in dark glasses, a baseball cap and a very wide, long fur coat. Londoners are inured to the strange. But I couldn't attract more attention if I was in a hijab, eating a bacon roll, downing lager, marching on the Orange Walk, and playing that well-known Protestant anthem 'The Sash' on the fucking bugle.

10.30pm

Basement flat, bars on the windows and several layers of curtains and blackout blinds. Open my coat to flash her on the doorstep.

'Hi Madam Titubana. I'm Anvar. What do you think?'

She has a Cleopatra cut. She's in her bare feet and a Jessica Rabbit basque. She's wound in so tightly, I swear her navel is peeking out over her cleavage.

'You make good effort. I show you dungeon now.'

Walk in. Take coat off. Look around. If I had known the dungeon was replete with power shower, L'Occitane soaps, clean towels, and a small bedsit and dressing area where I could change, I wouldn't have had to travel in the above kit.

'Dungeon up here.'

10.35pm

Up a small, crooked flight of stairs to enter a room with a heavy wooden door. It is a first floor dungeon.

Oh no, what have I done? What have I let myself in for? No way. I am gagging. What a smell, this is wild. It's a moist, sweet smell. But there's something not right.

What have I got myself into?

It reeks of blood, urine, the sweet scent of hard drugs and second-hand leather, stale and cracked with old human sweat.

Oh I am feeling sick. I feel really ill. I'm nearly heaving.

Mustn't do that. Must stay calm. And what is all this kit?

10.40pm

Looking around, pacing around the dungeon and touching the contents, a virgin to all I see.

To my right a cage, beside it an operating table which is covered in black, wipeable, shiny animal hide, below a rack.

A wheel on the wall, like a ship's, to activate the rack and hoist a human body. A scalextric of heavy lavatory chains, the kind to be found in an ironmonger's nearly tripping me up on the concrete floor.

There are shelves, drawers, and butcher's hooks, showcasing large and small implements that look like eyelash curlers but with spikes on.

Wow. It is freaky. Each and every space in the dungeon is occupied by a bewildering weapon; cat o' twenty tails to forty with knots in the strips, or balls of metal. Scalpels, scissors, a selection of slim and fat ten-inch needles, rubber gas masks, an oxygen cylinder, an anaconda of rope, riding crops, dildos, of every length and shape and thickness. A knife. Oversized tweezers. An arab strap. A metal scrotum harness. A ball of wire. A suction pump. What looks like a badminton racket but which fires off an electric shot when hitting a soft flesh target.

And a box like an old Carmen rollers set, leaking a couple of brown and blue wires, adapted to administering a different tone of ECT.

'I make all these myself, my own designs,' Madam Titubana is proudly explaining. 'These my tools. Worth many monies.'

'Are you insured?' I ask, thinking that the UN may be concerned about such an arsenal and send the troops in.

'NO!' We're shouting again. 'ME NO PAY TAX. ME INVISIBLE.'

'Do you have a bank account?' I query.

'NO. KEEP HUNDREDS OF THOUSANDS IN SUITCASE UNDER BED. ME NO LEGAL.'

And she is only paying me 80 smackers!

10.45pm

It is a Frankenstein of a play area.

Cotton buds, boxes of tissues of every ply and condoms of every flavour and colour and strength fight for hygienic attention against a regiment of baby wipes and face wipes.

There are a couple of bottles of spray bleach and some Dettol. It gets messy, I'm pondering.

'Get many surgical supplies from client who work hospital,' my host is explaining.

Am eyeing up the second bed, an operating table meets a dentist's chair. Yikes! Wish I could stop saying Yikes. I sound like Scooby Doo.

I can leave, I can leave, I can bail out!

Wish I hadn't called an editor and asked if he wants a piece on this. It would be called 'A Day In The Life Of A Dominatrix'. Really got to do it now.

10.50pm

Madam Titubana is holding up a strap-on. Okay, a minute ago, I was picking it up and checking it out, and yes, okay, I am mildly fascinated by it.

Sure I'll try it on. Yep, yep, that one looks okay, yep, like the, er, metal hoops on it, very nice, yes you have a great collection of, er, mock cocks.

I am SO not going to run out screaming!

Nope, can't, that's what she expects me to do, and I won't.

Millions of people do this kind of sexual practice all over the globe and there is nothing wrong with me trying it out. There could be something wrong with me if I like it, but I don't know what's going to happen with that yet.

Actually, come to think of it, that's not a very big strap-on, is it?

10.55pm

Oh rock 'n' roll, we are cooking with gas, this is the biggest knob I have ever seen, and if I am going to put it on I am damn well sure I'm going to have the biggest knob in town.

Madam Titubana's looking darkly sinister, quite the way I am beginning to feel.

Smell is minging tho' – keeps catching in my throat and out my nostrils where it's leaving a film on my nose hairs.

I am doing okay here. Am buckling this thing between my legs, it's like fighting with a saddle.

If I ask her for help it'll just confirm my innocence in these matters. At least I have not thrown up.

Where do these straps go? It's like fighting a mega squid.

Aha! Madam Titubana has stopped checking the security of her pulley and the safety of her dangling cage. Will she come over? Kind lady.

Oh that's how you do it. Yep, a bit tighter. I'm blushing. Thanks.

PRETTY WILD

11pm

Hallelujah! Am strutting around quite the thing. And now from this angle in the mirror, and now from this angle, and how about from here, how does it look from here? And casually walking past, you know, maybe strutting to some music, like some ragga, how does that fare? Hmm. Nice. Suit it actually. Think it looks quite chic, this one, in matt black.

11.05pm

I feel a completely perverse sense of excitement. Only had a cock for a few seconds yet while it was being attended to, even disinterestedly, I felt very, very powerful.

So this is what it's like to have a hard-on! This is what all the fuss is about; what men crave and seem apparently to be a slave to.

11.10pm

You know, I'm looking in the mirror here and think that perhaps for my build and broadness and everything, I should really have an even bigger one.

What a shame guys don't ever have such a choice.

Shit! What's that? The doorbell. He's here! He's here! Hi Ho, Hi Ho. Oh I hope I can do this.

'Anawar, what I call you?' Madam Titubana's asking.

'Er . . .'

'We don't get personal you know. Keep private.'

'Gina?'

'Ho-kay.'

I see.

A dominatrix does not expose herself or her life. Nothing or no one is that important it has to get personal. I like it.

Fuck, but 'Gina'? Anvar, that is so crap.

11.15pm

I dunno what I was expecting, but not laughter and warm voices. Banshee wailing maybe, a few screams.

Sounds like a tea party downstairs now.

I hear greetings not beatings.

Trying to get myself out of my strap-on.

11.20pm

When people know they're going to walk away they'll do anything. Exotic sex is addictive; going back to loving, sensitive sex is like being condemned to drink plain water if you feel more like yourself when you are an alcoholic. It's a thought.

11.25pm

I give up. I can't get out of this thing. Am trying to extricate myself from my new maleness. Fuck it. Never mind. Can't do it. Decide that I am going to look more excited than he is. Oh here's the boss.

'Gina?'

'Huh?'

'You go downstairs get "John". He taking coke.'

'Is he?' I ask, quite surprised.

'Clients spend too much on the drugs,' she's explaining, picking dust off one of the laminate covers.

'They want all this contact and off and out their faces also. I say drugs? Waste of monies. Silly buggahs. You down at half past, ho-kay?'

11.29pm

I wouldn't say I am a nice person, but I wouldn't say I am a truly bad person either.

No, I am not. Adventurous sure. And wanting to push the boundaries, still, which must be the teenager in me.

But think it's going to take a fair degree of nerve to mince down the stairs with an erection as if I've been doing it all my life.

11.30pm

Oh no, there he is! A skeletal, white-haired naked pensioner, balding and with a pot belly. It's like finding your grandad with his pants down at a wedding.

I just want to cover him up and make his apologies. Call him a cab and warn him that he can't come out without his clothes because people have standards and they don't want wizened penis with their after-dinner mints.

Harsh as it sounds, I really want him to sober up, express shock at his nudity and run out the door like a normal person.

Instead, like every good dominatrix, it looks like I will have to invent cruelties and instigate various abuses, because that is what he wants. The punters get what the punters want – and wow they're going to get it.

I'm bloody walking down the stairs like Danny La Rue here.

Going to start kicking my legs from side to side, need a top hat and cane.

Oh no, Anvar, don't giggle, no, don't laugh! Oh, must be the smoke from the crack, it's really potent, that, or I have first night nerves.

11.32pm

I am daring myself on, simple as that. That's why I'm here, I am trying to outweird myself in everything I do.

Oh but he looks so frail!

I gotta hand this to myself, this is an Oscar-winning moment.

Amazing how you have to act, and act well.

I mean, if you really want to hurt grandpa here for real then you are a deviant and probably a psychopath.

I just think I should help him find his babygro and rocking chair.

ANVAR KHAN

11.33pm

Anvar, you can do this, you can pull it off. I can act, I can be a sadist, I can will myself into that zone, where I am angry and I am brutal and I am volcano and I take no shit.

Go go go, get in there! Now!

Right I'm stalking the couch in what I feel is a very feline and predatory way, and I'm stroking a dog collar and leash, now I'm settling to stand behind him.

'You can call me Madam Gina,' I'm commanding.

'John' flings himself from the sofa and prostrates himself on the floor. 'Yes, mistress.'

Whoa! Sonny. Okay. All right.

Jeez, I mean, you don't have to be that much of a buffoon surely?

His enthusiasm is unsettling me. But of course, he knows the form. Any excuse, probably, to throw yourself at the feet of a bit of pussy in boots.

Thing is Anvar, you're looking at him and you are appalled, yes you are, you are embarrassed for his indignity. And this from a woman who is walking around in a wig, dark glasses and with a unisex pelvis.

11.34pm

'I said you can call me Madam Gina,' I'm insisting. Decide to slap the slabbed ground with the leash for dramatic effect.

'John' prostrates himself before me even more. I hope he hasn't got an arthritic hip.

'Yes, Mistress Gina.'

Gosh. Just imagine sitting in a sober state and being played back every drunken wanky thing you've ever said, or being forced to watch the time you puked on a stranger's shoulder on the way to the loo, and you'll know how squirmingly self-conscious I feel. Yet I do suddenly feel quite changed.

Bile is rising in me. He isn't listening.

'Listen to me, damn you! Address me as Madam Gina! Or I will punish you.'

'Sorry Madam, sorry, Madam Gina, sorry, so sorry. Can I have more coke please Madam Gina?'

Right, he can stick his mouth over that smoking gong again I suppose.

'That's enough,' I say.

'Thank you Madam Gina, thank you.'

'Good. Now I'm going to put a collar on you, you old bag, and lead you up to the dungeon on your belly like the dog you are.'

Stoned or not, if someone spoke to me like that I'd tell them where to go.

'Yes Madam.'

His knobbly knees are gingerly negotiating every splintered, wooden step.

'Come on you piece of crap!'

Hey, I am being extremely vicious here, berating him, tugging at his collar with the leash. Well, it's what he wants.

Oh no, I do feel a bit guilty.

I'm quite amazed at his response. I keep suspecting he may turn round and tell me to fuck off, any moment now, to stop this craziness. To regain his gentility.

'Yes, Madam. I am a piece of crap. Yes, Madam Gina,' he repeats.

This guy just can't be for real. But he is, and there are many like him or else Madam Titubana would work in an office for 12k.

11.40pm

Gotta get on with it. I am employed for two hours.

I am going to be a soldier about this, honour my uniform and hopefully avoid any casualties, however suicidal the enemy seems to be.

Reach the dungeon, undo the leash, slowly. Understand the

ritual and ceremony of S&M is as important as the emotional fulfilment.

Because, you know, this isn't about sex, this has fuck all to do with sex, this is about submission and allowing someone complete power and control over your physicality. Astonished at the amount of trust handed over to me and the Madam.

Okay, Madam Titubana is taking over and he is in the stocks immediately. He is being blindfolded, he is being given more coke, and Madam Titubana wants to me to stick my new cock in his mouth.

11.55pm

And now he's in the cage. Still blindfolded. Shackled to the bars by his hands and feet. He's growling and shrieking and raging like a chimp in a lab.

10 May
12.10am

The door of the cage is being opened, and 'John' is being released, only to be further shackled by Madam Titubana putting him on his knees and tying his hands behind his back. Oh, that looks pretty painful. 'John' howls as she attaches the knot of his wrists to a bar that she hoists three feet into the air.

'You have to know how much sore this is, this is so you not kill or maim the client,' she's telling me.

'No Dom want dead bodies in her dungeon, no. Not very professional.'

Ri-ight.

Better get some good copy out of this.

12.20am

'John' is let down off the bar, gets his hands back, gets the chains off his ankles and is allowed to lie down on the floor.

PRETTY WILD

12.23am

Nope, his wrists are being tied up with rope.

'Lie still!' Madam Titubana is shouting and tapping his temples with a riding crop.

'Now Gina, give me cushion.'

Bloody dark glasses mean I keep banging into racks and slithery, leathery things, it's like being underwater when everything is dried up, black and dead.

Get cushion. Madam puts it over 'John's' face.

'You sit on this?' she's asking me. What's this? A suffocation special?

'Sit?' she asks me again.

12.30am

Still inside the womb and nullified by drugs, 'John' is nodding at the operating table, and it's becoming apparent that he fancies this particular torture now.

12.35am

Madam Titubana is racking him out using rope and using the wheel on the wall to stretch him out even further. I am scurrying back and forwards carving off from a rock of crack and putting it in the bong for him, lighting it and letting him suck on it.

I'm getting fucking bored.

12.40am

'John's' screams and groans are very gratifying yet are bordering on noise pollution now.

We are moving him to what looks like an electric chair. I watch as Madam Titubana unties him, and then ties him up again. Takes a long time, all that knitting.

Thinking of some good jokes I can tell her.

12.50am

Madam Titubana is using cotton buds on 'John's' third eye.

'You see Gina, he can take three at a time.'

I actually feel a bit pressured now to be as much of a bully. Pick up what looks like a squash racquet. Place it tentatively on 'John's' thigh.

He screams! And screams! And rocks back and forward in the chair.

'Ha! Very good, you, ha ha ha, he like that, didn't you 'John'?'

'Aarrrgghhh, yes Madam, yes Madam . . . thank you Madam.'

Shit.

'What did I do?' I'm whispering to Madam Titubana.

'You gave him very high voltage electric shock!'

12.55am

'John' is now being untied and led like a prisoner to the next bed.

1am

'John' is being bound and gagged and his legs strung up towards the ceiling.

1.10am

'John' is being untied again. This S&M stuff, it's pure pedantry. All Boy Scout knots and camp queen dramatics. Madam Titubana is right. Being a dominatrix is incredibly dull. It is a very routine occupation.

1.25am

Tired, wanna go home. 'John' is now on his face on a leather sedan chair. He is tied up so his arse is in the air.

'You fuck him up the ass? Gina?'

'Please Madam Gina,' 'John' is crying. 'Please fuck me. PLEASE!'

1.30am

It was when he was initially racked up and screaming in pain, begging to be contorted, high on crack cocaine, with a dildo up his arse, hot needles on his nipples, and he was just about to shit himself, that it occurred to me that 'John' might have some emotional and psychological issues he needs to deal with.

Now he's getting up, all sober and surprisingly fresh-faced, smiling at me and Madam Titubana, mumbling something about can he have a shower? And thanks for a great session . . . then I see it.

'John's' penis is a mushroom, an apology of a fungus. Thought it was like that because of the elastic bands around his balls; but you know, this man can't get a hard on. He crawls on all fours because he cannot be *homo erectus*.

1.45am

'John' is taking me and Madam Titubana out for drinks in a club.

I think this is splendid and rather generous of him. A very civilised thing to do after the blood and pain of the past couple of hours.

Am so impressed with his chivalry I really feel quite disappointed with myself and decide that I should at least have devised some new and interesting tortures for him.

Feel I've lost face slightly.

'John' is very respectful of me.

Polite, almost obsequious.

And this man has a day job?

2am

Wonder if I could tell any of my friends what I have just done tonight, that I contributed to the terrorisation of another human being, and that we, well, he enjoyed it.

2.15am

Sitting in a private members club. Four quid for a half pint of lager.

'John' is paying. He is a nice guy. A single man – no wonder I think, given his impairment – and he is very successful, running his own company and is responsible for a workforce of 350 employees.

2.35am

More beers. 'John' is still paying. He will not speak directly to me that often, unless Madam Titubana goes to the ladies.

She waltzes off to reapply her blue glitter lippie. Ask 'John' why he likes pain.

'Known Madam Titubana for years, splendid woman, very lovely person, very trustworthy. Just think life is for living, do what you like to do. I love bondage. Just love it. Once you do it it's very difficult to give up. No, I've not got a girlfriend at the moment but I might be seeing someone soon. No, I'd never ask anyone else to do bondage with me, no one. I'd come to Madam Titubana. Never do it with anyone else. Too extreme, my girlfriends would never have liked it.'

3am

Drunk. Still high from passive coke smoking. Madam Titubana is talking about cardboard boxes with air vents in them, apparently they are the latest S&M craze.

Oh shit!

Just realised something.

I'm on *Richard and Judy* today.

No!

3.30am

In taxi. Great. A decent amount of cash in my wallet, won't have to visit the hole in the wall for at least a week.

Glad I kept my dark glasses and wig on tho', even in the club. Don't want 'John' calling a TV station and announcing what I've been doing. Mind you, you twat, Anvar, he trusts you and you must trust him. A client would never betray you, unless he is prepared to betray himself. This is the most honest relationship I've had for months.

Be funny I guess, Mr Junkie recognising me on the telly at some future date, like being on GMTV discussing the Top Ten best ways to flirt or why women cheat on their husbands, or something.

4am

Nodding off. Up in bloody eight hours. I mean, I like at least ten hours a day. Still, it's been a long day but at least I earned some moolah. Think about what Madam Titubana was saying.

She's in my thoughts, talking quickly. 'No dead bodies no, very bad, police come, then they know I is not legal! Very bad for business, you know!'

And 'John's' voice is ringing in my head too, against a backdrop of howls and sobs.

'You're reading too deeply into it, Gina. It's just fun. No, I don't have any childhood issues.'

Yes, but you have a very small one. And you hate yourself for it.

'Thing about bondage is once you start it you can't stop it. Very difficult to give up. Can't ask my girlfriend to do it.'

You can't get a woman, your penis is too small. You know that, that's why you want punished, don't you get that?

And Madam Titubana is gibbering on. 'Cardboard boxes, yes, very interesting, and you know I keep being asked to make people unconscious you know? Clients want me to put them out using gas, I say no, very dangerous, so thinking how to do this you know, to meet demand!'

Aaarrgghhh! Craziness, all around. Must be that perversion is normal. Well, hey Anvar, that would explain your actions tonight. Och, whatever. How can anyone smoke that shit? My head is shrinking, my brain feels like it's compressing into tiny macaroni pieces.

4.01am

All those naff women out there saying for a laugh that they are high class prozzies, they know nothing, NOTHING!

What's that about anyway? They trying to be sexy? Trying to make out a man would actually pay money for them? Christ, hope they don't think they'd just have to lie back and take it like they do in real life.

Oh, God, never again. No way. I am too savvy for this.

I know 'John' is a casualty, a sad wee man who likes being bossed for a while the way he has to boss people, but all his relationships must end in disaster as soon as he pulls his trousers down, women surely run away.

And that Madam Titubana is a greedy cow desperate for money and who is also a complete fucking sadist.

Well. Dunno if I want this as a wee part time job. Think it corrupts your humanity.

Mind you. I don't know why people complain they're broke; there's always the sex industry. I mean, knowing what I know now, I'll always work.

I Just Don't Care Anymore

12 May

7pm

On way to Bethnal Green to meet Vikram. Turns out he isn't a figment of my imagination and I did give him my number on the night I was barging and tripping around Soho wondering if I could ever go out with a woman. That was a waste of time, energy and money.

9pm

Vikram and I are smoking weed in bed. Shit he can talk.

'I mean I'm choosey you know, I don't just sleep with anyone. She has to be nice you know. Really ni-ice. The last woman I went with, she took me home and I just couldn't get it up. And she sits up right, and gets this book from a shelf, and starts reading me this chapter on impotent men, right, saying I'm emotionally insecure and I've got unresolved childhood issues and that it's really difficult for a man to make his way nowadays, and that he feels emasculated what with all these feisty women about . . . she starts asking me about my dreams and everything.'

'Ri-ight.' Issues, schmissues.

'So I skin up, yeah, and listen to her yeah? And I'm going that's it, you're right yeah, and the reason I couldn't get it up is because I'm not a slut. I just can't do it for anyone. I mean she has to be ni-ice. Know what I mean? I mean, you're ni-ice.'

'Ri-ight. Thanks.'

'I'm lying there, smoking my weed, and thinking, hey, miss, you're a boring bitch, c'mon girl, get it together, you ain't turning me on. You just ain't prepared to do the work baby. Because I'm a nice guy I just can't say those things you know? I mean I'm choosey. He's choosey. He likes you though. He

185

thinks you're ni-ice.'

'Thanks. Really chuffed. Cheers.'

'I've got something for you.'

Where's he off to? God I'm stoned. What is he doing? What's he got behind his back?

'I got something for you baby?'

He's holding a courgette. He looks pretty pleased about it too.

10pm

Roughest lover I've ever had. Try not to laugh.

'Suck me off.'

'Well I can't when you're holding my head over here by my hair.'

11pm

Eating pasta Vikram has made in a wok. He didn't use the courgette. Neither did I.

'We get back to the sex soon, yeah?'

He's standing up. Bit rude. Haven't finished my pasta.

'He thinks you're ni-ice.' In a baby voice. Fucking girl.

He's putting his cock onto the table. I put two slices of baguette at either side of it.

'Oh look Vikram, a still life.'

'You what?'

14 May
11pm

Vikram calls. Can't shake men off.

'What you wearing? You going to dress up ni-ice for me next time?'

Next time?

'In a kimono, socks, bra and sunglasses and working Vikram,

so can't talk, sorry.'

'Sunglasses, screen glare innit?'

'What do you want Vikram, told you we were only fun.'

'Lying here, skinning up, been to tai chi, been swimming, but he's lonely, wants you to come over.'

'Busy.'

'Know you're only using me, I like that, he likes it, but you never call me. Got this fantasy of you in a short skirt with a slit up the side. I'd dress up too for you.'

'In what, exactly?'

'Women like me to wear my builder's belt.'

I'm stunned.

'And me boots, turns 'em on.'

'Gotta go Vikram.'

'He keeps looking at me, goes soft and then hard, he doesn't know if you like him or not. He needs you, he likes you. He wants to meet your pussy again but you don't fancy him.'

Slam.

Text Vikram. Dump him. Never hear from him again.

Fridge Magnet Philosophy:
Fall in love with yourself, it's the only affair that will last.

16 May
10.30pm

In The Shadow Lounge in Soho.

Do a bit of pole-dancing. Bouncer tells Ramone to tell me to cool it. I'm frightening everyone.

Ramone objects and starts pole-dancing too. Swirls around the pole, but loses his grip and takes flight landing in the middle of the dance floor.

I'm watching this, laughing.

Picks himself up and runs holding his face in his hands to the gents. I follow him.

'You laughed you bitch, you laughed.'

'Ramone, it was funny.'

'No it wasn't it was so uncool. Anvar, I was up there for ages.'

'No, only a few seconds, no one noticed.'

'No, Anvar, I went through my whole life up there. I saw my birth, I was present at my funeral.'

More drinks. I'm chatted up by an Eastern European guy called, er, Lorca.

Taxi back to Ramone's flat. He has bevvie.

'Why are you over here, are your family poor? Do you live in a war zone?' I'm asking.

'Shut up Anvar, just shut up!' says Ramone still in trauma.

Have possibly the worst shag I've ever had. Lasts 30 seconds.

Start giggling, hysteria kicking in.

Lorca is pulling out his wallet. Shows me a photo of his family; sister, mother, father, dog and a sheep.

'You got visa?' he's asking me.

Order Lorca a cab.

Crash out to the sound of my moby ringing with a Glasgow number. Vaguely remember same number flashing at me before. Fucking Phantom Caller. Ignore it. No message.

Wake up an hour later. Ramone is sitting on the bed.

'Do you know what he does, that Lorca?' he's asking me.

'Nah, don't, don't care.'

'He's the cloakroom assistant in the Shadow Lounge.'

Oh no, I slept with a cloakroom attendant! And from that club! People go there to snag a celebrity. Arse. Can't go back there. Ever.

18 May

11pm

Back at The Shadow Lounge. They let me in. The red ropes
parted just like that. Ramone thinks they think I'm the cabaret.

Just slumming it now.

Becoming a sexual monster.

Done Madame Jojo's and a strip joint. Now on the prowl.

Ramone is hit on by youngster who looks like a pre-pubescent
Lenny Kravitz. American, half-Chinese, half-black. From NY.
Call him 90 cents.

'I don't want to be forward,' he's suddenly whispering in my
ear, 'but I could fuck the hell out of you.'

'But you're so young and you're gay,' I'm protesting.

'I'm as straight an arrow.'

'Not on the pull tonight. How old are you anyway?'

There are guys on earth who are meant to be gay because their
skin is dewy and their bodies are tight and he's one of them.

'I'm 21.'

Liar.

'Okay, I'm 19.'

Holy Mama.

'I'm old enough to be your mother,' I'm saying.

Why does that thought turn me on? I can be a Yummy
Mummy.

'That's cool.'

'And if we fuck, I'm a condom girl.'

'I'm a condom guy.'

Ten Kir Royales later. Well, he's legal.

Back to mine.

Got some Bacardi Breezers and a packet of crisps. Put crisps
out on a plate. Give him a piece of kitchen roll. 'Got any pizza?'

I'm feeding him. It's a first. So aware of how young he is.

'I feel sick, I've drunk too much,' says 90 cents and runs to
the loo.

Hear him retch. Oh he's coming back into the living room.
Looks bashful.

'I didn't make it,' he's saying.

Go to the loo and see three large splodges of cranberry on the
carpet.

'I'm sorry,' he's saying.

'It's okay,' I'm soothing. Mommie Dearest.

'Have you any mouthwash?'

1am

He is lying on top of me, dozily sucking my left nipple, and has
been for, yep, about half an hour. Admire him for it. Most guys
want to be that sexually vulnerable and never do it. Stroke his
hair. Maybe he just needs a mother.

It is like having your son's teenage friends round and one of
them sticks his hands down your knickers while you're putting
out the KFC bucket, and you don't know whether to slap him
or fuck him. Naughty, Freudian and erotic.

He fucks me like a man. Expert oral sex. Think they start
shagging in NY at twelve.

'What do you do at weekends?' Post-coital chat.

'Hang about in Harrow, in the park, smoking weed, and
doing a lot of fucking, know what I'm saying?'

Ri-ight.

'We just walk and chill. Maybe get a burger, check out some
sneakers . . . do a little skateboarding, listen to some tunes . . .'
Worry that he might be stealing sports shoes and dealing crack.
Wonder if I should call his real mother or at least social services.

3am

Wake up. He fucks me until 3pm the next day without coming.
No joke. He strokes and caresses me. Massages my eyeballs,
which is weird but pretty adventurous as foreplay I feel, and
excellent for my hangover.

Goodbye Stand-By Shags

21 May
2pm
Sitting writing. Nibbling crackers.

3pm
Moby rings. It's Mikey, and so what, exactly? Pick up.

'Anvar hi, how are you?'

'Tell me something Mikey, why did you never tell me you are married?'

Silence.

'So, you know.'

'Yep, I do. Found your wedding ring in your pocket.'

'You went through my pockets? That's not on.'

Outrage isn't valid here.

'Was looking for a lighter.'

Silence. A sigh.

'Well?'

'Look Anvar, we were just having fun, you knew that.'

No I didn't.

'And look, you know, you're a smart woman, you are mature, you aren't looking for a man to fall in love with, you aren't interested in men that way, you just like fucking around and I think that's great. I admire you for it. And I knew you were like that. I thought you understood there would never be anything more serious between us, so why would I tell you about Maggie . . .'

'Don't fucking say her name to me, Mike!'

'Okay, okay, I didn't mention my wife because I knew, like you knew, that we weren't going to get involved.'

I'm chewing on more crackers, spluttering on crumbs.

'Mike, tell me something, why do men choose a woman like me to fucking lie to?'

'I guess, I guess . . . well . . .'

He's struggling, bit rich of him to do that, a bit of self-analysis wouldn't go amiss here.

'You're a good-time girl Anvar. You will never get serious about any man.'

5pm

Thinking of having some cheese.

Oh, here he is.

'Hi Anvar, Giles here.'

'Uh-huh.'

'You okay?'

'Yep.'

'Anvar, got an idea for an article for you . . . really liked that piece on being a Dominatrix, but, you know, bit too hardcore for our magazine, but if you could lighten it up . . .'

Lighten up? He's asking me to lighten up?

'Giles, can I ask you something?'

'Sure, fire away.'

'Tell me, why didn't you call me, after that night at your pad?'

He might spill on the fanny farts thing Anvar; you gotta be prepared for that girl, could be mortifying all over again.

'Anvar. Shit. Okay. Can you handle it?'

I snort with derision.

'I was seeing someone, had been for three weeks. Look Anvar, I have very specific ideas about the type of woman I want, and you are a very strong woman you know? But I like, well, blondes, very English middle-class blondes, who are shall I say, less challenging and more docile than you.'

Can't do Satanic Princess To Sloane.

PRETTY WILD

7pm

Might make some salad.

Who's this on the moby?

Aw, it's 90 cents.

'Hey.'

'Hey.'

'You alright?'

'Yes, you stopped being sick?'

'Hahahha, well, I was not myself that night.'

'What are you doing?' I'm asking. He really needs a social worker.

'Got an audition for a boy band, was hoping you could call them, maybe put in a word for me? You being a journalist and all that? I mean, huh, I could come around and make it worth your while . . . I mean, what we did, well, you can have that again . . . all day . . .'

Ah, youth. A teenage man and a thirtysomething woman. It's a sexual match. But I say goodbye to 90 cents. I do not need to feel as old as I am and I will never be as young as this man I was feeling.

10pm

In a bar, drinking coffee, with my neighbour who runs an art gallery. Meet one of her friends, a hippy with rather startling eyes. She comes over and sits down with us and won't stop staring at me.

Aw come on woman, leave it out. I feel pretty sore about things nowadays, pretty done in, pretty damn tired and bored and cynical and tough and pretty fed up feeling all those things too.

'You have a secret admirer Anvar; you already know the man you will spend the rest of your life with.'

That's all I need. Some quack telling me I am either doomed or destined to be in love. Aye right. 'Twould be a miracle.

25 May

Wake up in the bathroom. It's the middle of the afternoon – what the hell am I doing here lying on the floor with toilet roll stuck in my mouth?

Rescue me.

The Etiquette Of The Orgy

3 June
6pm
Patrick calls suddenly. Fancy coming to a sex club in Manchester? Could be an article in it for you. Yeah, s'pose, whatever. Don't know anyone who isn't a sleazebag.

Long journey mind.

Introduced to Drew and Jerry and Hilda. Yeah, how are you, pleased to meet you, yep, let's go then, bit of a drive from London huh?

Don't mind if I take a nap do you?

And I'm off to Snoozeville, lovely.

6.45pm
Wake up to sounds of moaning.

Jerry is massaging Hilda's breasts as she sits in the passenger seat, she is wanking Patrick who is driving, and talking on the hands-free, and Drew is trying to convince me to join in.

Nah. I'll just watch, I say.

Fall asleep again.

I mean, I'm trying to nap. Can't you lot keep it down?

7.15pm
Pull into a service station and decide on burgers and chips for five. 'I don't want a pickle on mine,' Drew's saying.

'Well, I'll have your pickle,' says Hilda, 'I love pickles.'

'You'll have to put your clothes on to go in,' I'm pointing out.

'No chips for me,' says Jerry, 'I'm on a diet.'

'Aw, have some chips,' says Drew.

'No, they don't agree with me mate,' Jerry's patting his stomach.

'Anvar do you want chips?'

I get out and go into the fast-food chain that dare not speak its name. Well, I am the only one who is fully dressed.

Think what marks group sex out from one-to-one sex is greed, why have one when you can have them all?

11pm - Manchester.

I see a fat bespectacled woman flabby and naked with long straggly grey hair, like she's just taken it out of a scrunchy, lying on a bed in the corner of the main bar, with four men, one stroking and kissing her nipples, another snogging her, one giving her oral sex and masturbating her, and the other snuggling in looking for something to do.

I look around the room, everyone is naked or wearing underwear; some of the men are in swimming trunks. Order bottles of water from the bar. Figure we are the youngest here, looks like SAGA to Shagger in one easy move.

On the movie screen three women are working a dildo between them.

'That's pure quality,' Drew's saying, mesmerised.

'Would you do that Anvar?' Jerry's asking me.

'Always fancied wearing a strap-on and taking a man up the ass,' I hear myself saying.

'Oh, I'm not sure about that,' huffs Drew, as he shivers. Result – I mean, just leave me alone.

Look around and yawn.

By the startled and flushing faces of the clientele, it seems you can get a fuck here by maintaining eye contact for two seconds.

Not interested.

Crap white house 5% proof wine. No one is allowed to get drunk. Anyone who behaves 'offensively' is asked to leave.

Couples are here; guys wearing nipple-clamps and her in nightie, sitting quietly on their own watching the big TV.

Swingers are just so ugly and have the personalities of a lentil.

More women here than men; guys walk up to wives and mothers and ask to feel their breasts or touch their pussy and then go off to a private room. The husband is left looking uninterested, with his soda.

Have a walk around.

There are cubicles you lock from the inside with a grate at the top of the door you can slide shut, like warders look through when they ask you to sober up and if you want tea. No, I mean, that has never happened to me, ever, not yet.

11.45pm

Bottles of flat pop sit randomly on the pool table and on the ledges around the sauna. Drew takes a sip.

'Nothing's happening,' he's saying. He takes another gulp. 'The women are a bit too shy, eh?'

A woman with post-pregnancy breasts runs over to him and grabs the bottle. Drew turns away in case she tries to molest him.

No, she's giving him a row.

The bottle is contaminated with liquid ecstasy.

Oh shit.

12.30am

Drew is a crazed maniac. Jerry takes a secret photo of him using his phone camera. Drew is shagging a 75-year-old pensioner. She comes too.

Think this is what extreme porn channels are for, or magazines. No one wants to see it 'live'.

I am so out of this, so detached and feeling so disappointed that I don't feel like joining in and having it off with any of these sorry specimens.

I mean, maybe I've just had too much sex in my life and I am failing to see what the attraction is now.

12.45am

Wander into an open orgy.

'You dirty fucking bastard,' a woman is screaming.

'We'll have none of that,' says the man's wife.

This is a sophisticated forum and there is no room for slander even of the excited careless kind, and even when you are shagging someone's partner, you can't talk dirty, it's disrespectful apparently.

12.50am

Hear voices. Jerry and Drew and Patrick working a room containing two women.

'Nice big piece you got there,' Drew's saying to one of the men.

'Your wife is a great fuck mate, well done,' Jerry's saying to the other bloke.

Oh Lord, it can't be true, and yet it is and how predictable too.

Guys shaking each other's hands and congratulating each other on a job well done, all to appease each other.

Great politics, the etiquette of the orgy; all friendly and backslapping because having another man's woman, well, you could end up in a fight.

12.55am

Wandering, drink is shit, water is warm, everyone is desperate and I have gone right off sex.

'Get your hand off Shane's butt,' asks a woman of her husband. Aha. I mean, at least you take your jealousies and gripes back home and deal with them there.

1am

Typical. I go to a sex club and start talking to people and asking them about what they do, listen to their problems and give them advice about their relationships.

Man with a handlebar tache, wife naked but wearing several strings of beads and her watch.

'How can you let your wife sleep with other guys?' I'm asking. 'My wife isn't my property,' he's saying. Confidently.

Uh-huh.

'You must have a really secure marriage not to get jealous?' I'm pushing. Well, what is going on here? Dear reader, don't you want to know? Because I do.

'Most marriages split up over infidelity, that's not going to happen to us. If I can watch my wife fuck another guy and not feel aggressive and want to punch his lights out then as a man I am free, I am not an ogre, I am liberated from what constitutes all men.'

Shit that sounds almost noble.

2am

Wanna go home! Now! Having to sit and watch naked old people sit and watch telly is not a spectator sport.

Hear sex going on. Look around. In the corner, beside the mantelpiece, the one with photographs of sea views on it.

Spy a woman with tears in her eyes as she watches her man fuck another woman, right now, in front of her.

Sexual freedom my arse. This is emotional abuse.

Have I been doing the same? For a long time now, it seems. Ignoring my emotions for a fuck?

3am

In car back to London. Finally.

Drew is still gibbering, well, he took what sometimes constitutes a date rape drug by bloody accident. I may have woken up at times appalled at what I have done, but wait till he sees the photo.

'That was my first fuck since I got married. It's a big thing that. Once you've taken those vows. The first shag after that, it's a big thing.'

Oh Lord.

Realise I'm the only person here who is single.

7am

In bed. Alone. Get up. Write.

To men no relationship is real until it's cast in the stone of a religious vow, even when those involved aren't religious. Marriage is when a man thinks he's a better man than he is, and thinks he can do monogamy. He cheats himself. He cheats on you.

Why You Shouldn't Lose Your Anal Virginity On A One Night Stand With A Stranger

7 June

2pm

Actually thinking of becoming a Buddhist nun. Going to Thailand, sitting in the sun, meditating, washing my crimson robes in the river.

Nah. Bad habits are hard to break.

5pm

In pub. With Heidi. Drunk. Three bottles of Merlot down.

Talking about anal sex.

She's done it, and the woman we have accosted for cigarettes says she's done it. Love how women can just talk about anything.

Swear I've never done it. Never would. I mean, you hear so many horror stories; guys being really rough and women being cut, it's awful. I mean, why allow it at all? It's not for women. I mean. Do we have a clitoris on our bums?

Heidi and her new mate are looking at me, scunnered.

'Anvar you think too deeply about stuff.'

7pm

Big man, big smile. Very London chat up line. Down here, I mean, it's a heady cultural mix.

'Anvar, you mixed race Asian? Huh. You're one of my tribe.'

Deals in antiques, travels around the world buying and selling. Half Nigerian.

8pm

Back at mine for more red wine. The usual routine, except –
'I need to check something out on ebay,' he's saying. 'You
online?'

'Sure. But like what?' I'm asking, wondering what could be on
sale that is more exciting to procure than me.

'I collect memorabilia,' he's saying. 'Pieces from the time of
slavery. Art. Here's something.'

It's a poster of a black face advertising cocoa, cotton and
chocolate drops.

'I've even got an ankle cuff that belonged to a child slave.'

Forget about the nun thing, I am going to re-train as a
counsellor.

'That's creepy,' I'm saying, a remark more often heard after
we actually get down to it and random desires are expressed.

'No,' he's saying. 'It's beautiful.'

11pm

In bed. On bed. Being chased around bed, and nearly falling off
bed.

Think it's funny that we share heritage, to be factual, between
us, there's actually a white person in the bed too. Feel that my
honky half just shouldn't be messing with someone who is so
messed up about black repression.

He's actually making me feel more white than I've ever felt.
I am as embarrassed as a Scot who made their wealth flogging
Kunta Kinte's cousins.

11.30pm

Okay. To be honest, Solomon has a cock that could stand up a
four poster bed. I'm sure not all black men are well-endowed,
because I haven't slept with all black men, but then again I
haven't slept with a black man who isn't.

Try to concentrate on a two-hand wank, and to get my

mouth around at least a third of his exocet missile, yet even with my years of training I feel inadequate. Worry about getting more lines around my mouth. He'd drive you to botox.

Oh. I'm climbing his frame like a child about to lose her balance.

And what is he talking about?

It's dawning on me that he is muttering away to himself.

'Oh yes, now you're . . . it's big, so big, yes baby . . .'

Hold on a mo', here. Say what?

Am sitting on top of him and pressing my ear to his mouth to listen.

'Oh and now you're astride me, oh isn't my cock big? It's so big. It's bigger now. Oh now you're kissing my neck, oh baby, now you're nibbling my ear. Oh, you're pumping up and down, oh yes! Baby, baby, now you're moving slowly. Oh yes. On my big co-ock.'

Dear reader, I wonder if he will actually still try to narrate events when his mouth is demanded in another area.

'Sitting, humff, oh, huh, on, on, hmm, sitting, aw! Arrggh! On my, humff, humff, face!'

Yep. He is.

12.10am
On all fours on the bed.

'Anvar, do you take it up the ass?'

Leap off bed in fright.

No!

'You mean you are an anal virgin?'

Yes! Yes I am!

'Wanna try it?'

No fucking way.

'Why not?' he's asking.

'Because,' I'm saying, holding my dressing gown over my body in fear. 'Because . . . because . . .'

Because what Khan? You want to save yourself for a man who matters? Actually, maybe, yes, yeah, perhaps I do want to do that, perhaps I just don't trust men enough to give that away.

Solomon is chancing it. The sneak.

Or perhaps I know, deep down, as every woman does, that this is a special favour to a guy, and I sure as hell ain't going to grant it to some man I'll be putting out with the rubbish in the morning. Nah.

'Because, I have piles,' I say. 'Bad ones, big grape things, nasty. Not sexy.'

I mean, really.

'Tell you what Sol,' I'm saying. 'I'll let you take me up the ass, if I do it to you first.'

Lord, he looks as if he's just been shot. Perhaps most men who want anal have homosexual fantasies, he could be closing his eyes and dreaming of Rock Hudson for all I know. Don't see why a man should want to do to you what he won't accept himself. Oh yeah, I forgot. Silly moi.

They think every woman should provide a comprehensive sexual service, without realising that they are in your bed because it suits you and you alone.

'I'm not comfortable with that,' he's panicking. Result. He's gone all jittery. Funny how his request doesn't interfere with his masculinity but me asking for some equality in bed does.

Now that I've mentioned the possibility of a woman enjoying taking a man up the old crack, it's like I've just accused him of being gay.

Huh.

12.30am

Solomon is leaving, no more wine thanks, he's driving. He tells me he's glad to have shagged me because I can handle the size of his cock.

I mull over what it is like to be Sol, constantly worrying if women can take it, carefully alive to a pick-up who looks as broad and as strong as his best friend.

Background, colour or profession – it doesn't matter. Men are just one big rainbow people with no gold at their end, and there's no way they are going to find it at mine.

10 June
9am

Up, sprightly and early, writing away, haven't been drinking, ain't been shagging, am in serious detox and actually pretty happy. Big radio and TV plans as London is being kind.

La la la . . . oh, moby's off. Don't get that number. Ah! It's that Glasgow number again. The Phantom Caller. Think I scrubbed messages before inadvertently. Oh well. Can't be personal. All men have been dumped and I am off the wagon from the flooze.

'Hi Anvar, it's me. It's me Anvar. Anvar? Anvar . . . been trying to get you to answer for months . . . Anvar . . . can you talk? It's me. Anvar, my love . . . my love . . .'

SEAMUS!

Oh shit, my world has stopped. It's like I'm still, I don't feel the speed of it turning so fast. I know. I KNOW. Oh shit. Oh SHIT! I know, I know. It's him. I know he has come to get me.

9.01am

He's still on the phone.

The memory hurts. That day. It is still there, hanging like a bat in my heart.

'Anvar . . .'

Oh the anger! It is roaring out of me. Like sick from a woman possessed.

'Look mate, I dunno why you are suddenly calling me after all these months, I mean, you know, I am in London now, and you know, mate, I have a life, I have a career, I have a wardrobe I have invested a great deal of time and money in, and I live in London and those clothes are not going to waste, I mean, I'm happy, I have friends, new friends and I am just about to meet one of them, Anna, for dinner actually, later, and you, you . . . I'll tell you what you did! You, you married someone else! You married someone else, a woman, who isn't me, and you just call me up like this and think I will jump and . . . I never thought I would see you again . . .'

I am crying, bloody weeping.

'And . . . I never thought . . .'

Silence. And it's, for once, a soothing, caressing silence that I feel I can burst into, like I am running into the light.

'Anvar, I am so sorry. I understand this is a shock. Anvar, please. Just give me a minute, a second of your time. Anvar, please.'

And I hear a quality in his voice that floors me.

'If you have any feeling for me, anything at all, please, we have to talk.'

Am hiccupping like a wee girl.

'No, can't get my head around this. Go away.'

Slam. Too much practise.

7pm

At Mr Kong's, Chinatown.

'What happened between you and him?' Anna's asking. She senses something is up. Something new in me, she sees it.

I can't eat. That'll be it. No room for an extra meal. No little corner.

I'm too weak, even, to lift a prawn cracker.

'Seamus was my friend for years. Tried to tell me he was in love with me. Huh. I remember that very night, he went off on one, began a big speech about how he was engaged and I was with his mate, and I thought he was on to me, you know, sensed I was attracted to him, and was going to let me down gently, so I ran out his flat . . . never spoke of it again.

'Well. You know. They way he . . . held me, you know, goodbye hugs and all that, held me like I was the most precious woman in, well, the . . . world, I guess . . . anyway, I brushed him off. Well, you know me, no commitment gal and all that. Oh yeah, and I was going out long term with one of his mates, did I say that?'

Anna is looking at me curiously.

'And well . . . he got married. Me and his mate split up . . . well . . . all in the past I guess.'

Anna puts down her glass.

'Jesus Anvar, I . . .'

'We had one night together. I stole him for one night Anna. And it wasn't sex, what happened between us. Of all women I know the difference . . . It was too late, you see, when I finally realised that he is and was then, the only man I have ever truly liked, and when I look back I see how I behaved with him, how keen I was to be in his company, and then, got jealous when he got wed. It's madness. I feel . . . I mean, when he called today I had this feeling, like I never knew . . . oh, I just don't know who I am anymore.'

Anna is staring at me.

'Anvar, do something for me.'

'What?'

'Talk to him.'

17 June

You may think of what kind of person would set your pulses racing like Thumper at the dogs. As we can organise a fridge or accessorise a room, us gals, well, we can sure as hell design a possible guy.

Yet the great procurator Sod, he has his own laws, and they touch us all.

You can never prepare for the big love or second guess his arrival. You will never conjure him up, or even dream of him accurately. He drops out the damn sky. And you will be squashed. You may know him already, or you may not. But you will recognise him, and in this way he will not be a stranger.

1 July
2pm - Glasgow

Right, meeting him at 3pm, round the corner so that leaves me an hour to walk that, er, 15-minute walk, stroll really.

Oh Anvar, don't you learn?

Never pack a suitcase when you are drunk.

The hideousness of my ensemble is SO apparent. This is the biggest date of my fucking life, my entire fucking life, and I have nothing to wear that matches!

Arse!

This is not what a girl wants to accept at such a critical point in her romantic career.

Oh, bugger, right, the little black dress and black boots and damn this eyeliner! Can usually put it on so straight and just flick it up at the lids like that, so! No. Cotton wool, where is it?

No, it's sticking to my fingers, I am sweating, ugh! That's no good. More perfume.

Okay. Perfect. Look a tad flustered. Oh no I have a blotch! Aarrrgghh! A damn heat spot on my cheek! Out out damn blotch!

2.02pm

Ready to leave. Door's not working. What? Why not?

Keys are in the lock aren't they? Duh! Anvar, you've locked it you twat. I think.

Oh no, key's not turning. I'm trapped. I've locked myself in. No! Not now! Not after all those years! Shit!

Maybe I should call the police. What's that number again? Nine . . . something. I mean, fate's not going to intervene again is it? And stop me?

Oh! Try again. Slowly now. That's it.

Thank the Lord!

Know there's a direct line to the emergency services but hell, right now, I can't remember it. I'm sure they're grateful.

2.03pm

Right, I am charming, in, er club gear, with a yellow handbag, and with 50 minutes to spare, yes, that's right, I mean I can just smoke to pass the time.

Aarrgghh! No! Need fags. Oh what a nuisance! I just can't cope with this at all! The stress of it.

Okay, I'm checking the road for traffic, and I am not daring to make a move until it is clear for a mile either way. I mean, I am that fragile at the moment.

'Take care getting to me,' he'd said.

Okay, crossed road, in the shop. Hi! Yes hi! I'm well, yes, I really, really am. Huh? London? Yes I live there. Oh great place, really smashing. Yes? Who? Oh Richard and Judy, they're fine, really well in fact, thanks for asking.

What do I need? Pardon?

Oh yes, 60 Marlboros please. Yep. Oh shit, and a box of matches, yes, just the one, got a lighter but you know, can't find it. Where am I going? Today? Right now?

Oh I'm going to the bridge, in the park, yes. Many thanks, bye. No can't stay for a cup of tea, no, no, don't have time, must get to the bridge now! Kelvin walkway! Yes! Bridge!

'Oh, that poor lassie, Anvar,' I'm sure I hear them mutter. 'I hope she's not going to throw herself off it. London must be so stressful. She used to be such a nice girl.'

2.05pm

Oh this is a time of sudden mishaps and near death experiences!

Right, cross road, avoided that ESSO tanker – just didn't see it coming.

This is the longest walk of my life.

Am bouncing like a thunderbird puppet in heels down the tarmac slope to that bloody bridge.

Oh I am so slow today! What time is it?

Got less than an hour to go. He'll be on time won't he? Now, when so much time has been wasted by us being apart?

2.10pm

Right. I'm here. Hands shaking. Bloody matches spilling out everywhere.

I'm lit. Good.

Calm down Anvar. Yogic breathing.

2.25pm

Back here, home, in Glasgow. Funny. I remember now that there are photographs of me as a baby who has just learned to walk, where I'm hanging onto the railings of a bridge down beside the bandstand of Kelvingrove Park, down a bit, over there, and here, in the West End of Glasgow, a precious place to me where you can scrape my DNA off the pavements.

Weird huh? As a toddler I could never have known that 35 years later, I would again be standing on a bridge, right now, in the same park, and find myself again clutching at the bars, to steady me, waiting for a man now, a man I have wanted and waited for all my puff, and a man I know will alter the course I have set myself.

I'm ready.

PRETTY WILD

2.45pm

I just have to be still, I just have to wait here and it will all be okay. Nervous, really nervous.

What the hell is that racket? Oh no. NO! It's too much!

There's a guy playing a piccolo karaoke somewhere on a bench up there.

Shut up!

ARSE!

Now people in pairs and families are walking past me.

Oh walk on, walk on . . . bye, get out my face . . . I don't want to see or hear anyone, just him.

Oh that's it, just stand beside me and gibber.

Didn't know how much fun and pleasure folk get out of throwing bread to ruddy moorhens.

'Oh, look, look, the pigeon's taken off, a-a-a-a-hhhh. Tell you what, let's throw a stick at this end and see if it comes out the other. Wheeeee! See, that's the swan's nest there. Oh, it's been desecrated. Shame. Oh, look at the moorhen wiggling its neck. Throw some more pan loaf, David. Oh look, there's a squirrel.'

2.52pm

If I had an AK47, well, there's no coincidence it bears my initials . . . I want the world to stop. Stop! I want everyone to quit laughing, and cheering and playing the fucking piccolo. How dare they. Don't they know? Like I know?

3pm

There's a man hurrying down the path to my left, down the slope, waving at me, I've dropped my bag, my fag's fallen, it's him.

It's him. It's Seamus.

Oh my darling.

10 July
4pm

Tea and a Tunnocks teacake. Thinking.

The adventures and lessons I have had so far stay with me. They have helped me judge how this romance is right for me. Helped me know this man is true.

I mean, girls, guys and readers, I've lost my heart, but I have not lost my mind.

I always toasted to health, wealth, sex, love and happiness. I figured that covered it. Now the last word comes first.

What I have been has not been a lie. I liked the power of being able to fuck and go, I said yes more often than no, I am the archetypal bad girl, and you know what? Even bad girls get the prize.

It's just that even sex is better now that his huge hand has come out the sky and picked me up by my fur lapels, and whisked me away into those big arms I remember always held me in tenderness, friendship and respect and love.

It's true what they say, and I ain't too proud to admit it now. You know when you have met 'the one'.

It has been the longest walk of my life. Finding him. And now that I'm here, now that I'm actually here, I'm stopping where I am.

Waking Up With Mr Right

13 July
10am

It's my birthday today! I am 37. What's that? Tea? Sure, lovely.

Oh, I feel like a cigarette. Need a lighter babe. What? In your pocket? Okay, I'll look for it.

Gotta make calls today, get this TV drama on the road. Yep! Yes, darling, I'm a bit hungover, yeah, oh I know, I lean on the fridge when I'm trying to come to my senses.

No, Seamus, I'm not going to puke. Never do. Can't remember the last time I did . . .